HANDBOO]

❖

NUMBER SEVI

Hawes

First Steps for Problem Solvers

A guide to Junior
Mathematical Olympiads

Mary Teresa Fyfe
and
Andrew Jobbings

The United Kingdom Mathematics Trust

First Steps for Problem Solvers

© 2015 United Kingdom Mathematics Trust

Published by The United Kingdom Mathematics Trust.

Maths Challenges Office, School of Mathematics, University of Leeds, Leeds, LS2 9JT, United Kingdom

http://www.ukmt.org.uk

First published 2015

ISBN 978-1-906001-25-4

Printed in the UK for the UKMT by The Charlesworth Press, Wakefield.

http://www.charlesworth.com

Typographic design by Andrew Jobbings of Arbelos.

http://www.arbelos.co.uk

Typeset with LATEX.

The books published by the United Kingdom Mathematics Trust are grouped into series.

The EXCURSIONS IN MATHEMATICS series consists of monographs which focus on a particular topic of interest and investigate it in some detail, using a wide range of ideas and techniques. They are aimed at high school students, undergraduates and others who are prepared to pursue a subject in some depth, but do not require specialised knowledge.

1. *The Backbone of Pascal's Triangle*, Martin Griffiths

2. *A Prime Puzzle*, Martin Griffiths

The HANDBOOKS series is aimed particularly at students at secondary school who are interested in acquiring the knowledge and skills which are useful for tackling challenging problems, such as those posed in the competitions administered by the UKMT and similar organisations.

1. *Plane Euclidean Geometry: Theory and Problems*, A D Gardiner and C J Bradley

2. *Introduction to Inequalities*, C J Bradley

3. *A Mathematical Olympiad Primer*, Geoff C Smith

4. *Introduction to Number Theory*, C J Bradley

5. *A Problem Solver's Handbook*, Andrew Jobbings

6. *Introduction to Combinatorics*, Gerry Leversha and Dominic Rowland

7. *First Steps for Problem Solvers*, Mary Teresa Fyfe and Andrew Jobbings

The PATHWAYS series aims to provide classroom teaching material for use in secondary schools. Each title develops a subject in more depth and in more detail than is normally required by public examinations or national curricula.

1. *Crossing the Bridge*, Gerry Leversha

2. *The Geometry of the Triangle*, Gerry Leversha

The PROBLEMS series consists of collections of high-quality and original problems of Olympiad standard.

1. *New Problems in Euclidean Geometry*, David Monk

The YEARBOOKS series documents all the UKMT activities, including details of all the challenge papers and solutions, lists of high scorers, accounts of the IMO and Olympiad training camps, and other information about the Trust's work during each year.

Contents

Series Editor's Foreword

This book is part of a series whose aim is to help young mathematicians prepare for competitions at secondary school level. Here the focus is on the section B questions from the Junior Mathematical Olympiad papers. Like other volumes in the Handbooks series, it provides cheap and ready access to directly relevant material. All these books are characterized by the large number of carefully constructed exercises for the reader to attempt.

I hope that every secondary school will have these books in its library. The prices have been set so low that many good students will wish to purchase their own copies. Schools wishing to give out large numbers of copies of these books, perhaps as prizes, should note that discounts may be negotiated with the UKMT office.

London, UK   GERRY LEVERSHA

About the Authors

Mary Teresa Fyfe gained her mathematics degree from the University of Glasgow. She has taught in several secondary schools in the West of Scotland, including 33 years as a Head of Department at Saint Bride's Secondary and Hutchesons' Grammar.

She regularly provides in-service training for teachers on methodologies to inspire able young mathematicians. She has been involved in many aspects of the work of the UKMT, including being the Director of the National Mathematics Summer School for many

years, initiating the Team Maths Challenge, setting problems for
Olympiads, and initiating Mathematical Circles.

Andrew Jobbings gained both his BSc and his PhD in mathematics from
Durham University. He taught mathematics for 28 years, including
14 years as Head of Department at Bradford Grammar School,
before founding the publishing business Arbelos.

With a keen interest in providing mathematics enrichment activities,
Andrew devises problems for the UKMT and is involved with many
other UKMT projects. He has regularly chaired a problems group
for the European Kangaroo contest and gives Royal Institution
masterclasses.

Preface

One key goal of this book is to provide some understanding of what it means to write out carefully a solution to a problem, something that pupils are often not used to doing. More generally, the book aims to be an informal guide for anyone wishing to tackle mathematical problems of a more challenging nature, some of whom may be potential JMO candidates.

The problems on the Junior Mathematical Olympiad (JMO) papers are intended to be challenging and thought-provoking. They probably look unusual, so that it is not immediately obvious how to solve them, in contrast to a typical question from a school text-book. However, though the problems may appear unfamiliar, the mathematics involved in the solutions should be familiar to most good young mathematicians of an appropriate age.

The solutions to each year's problems are provided in the 'official' solutions booklet, but these have been worked on by a group of people to produce a polished result, and are not intended to be 'model' solutions. There is no attempt to show how a solution might be discovered, nor all the work that was done on scrap paper!

Acknowledgements

The UK Junior Mathematical Olympiad was started by Tony Gardiner in 1989, some years before the UKMT was founded. Many people have been involved in the JMO since it began, including problem setters, markers and teachers in schools. All of them, especially Tony, deserve thanks for their help and support over the years of the competition.

Special thanks are due to Steven O'Hagan and Alan Slomson, who have helped us enormously in all sorts of ways. We should also particularly like to thank the following, who most helpfully commented on early drafts:

Clara Fyfe; Alastair and Calum Kilgour; Jane Ritchie; George and Stephen Power. There is no doubt that the book has improved immeasurably as a result of their suggestions. Gerry Leversha's guidance as editor has also been invaluable.

Of course, any remaining mistakes are entirely the responsibility of the authors, each of whom reserves the right to blame the other!

Glasgow and Chipping Norton, UK   MARY TERESA FYFE
Baildon, Shipley, UK   ANDREW JOBBINGS

Chapter 1

Introduction

A good problem is one that mixes order and chaos in a deep and subtle way, and that fires the imagination for that reason. Perhaps another way to say this is that in solving a good problem, one discovers some wonderful and totally unexpected regularity, when one expected nothing and on first sight saw only a jumble.

Douglas Hofstadter
from *Games and Mathematics* by David Wells

What do you need to be able to do in order to be a successful problem solver? How can you achieve this goal?

We hope that using this book will help you to answer the first question. Our answer to the second, of course, is "use this book"!

1.1 Layout of the book

After the opening chapters the book is divided into two parts: the first looks at problems; and the second is for reference.

Part I

Part I is the key part of the book. It includes all the problems that were set[*]
between 1999 and 2015 for section B of the Junior Mathematical Olympiad
(see chapter 3 for an explanation of the JMO). Note that the problems
from 1989 to 1995 are contained in *More Mathematical Challenges* by Tony
Gardiner.

Each problem is included either as an example or as a question in
an exercise, where it is labelled with its position on the original paper;
you should find a question labelled B1 or B2 significantly easier than one
labelled B5 or B6.

The problems have been divided into different categories, loosely based
on the skills and techniques required. Some of the problems use ideas
from more than one area of mathematics, so the authors have chosen what
seems to them to be the most appropriate place.

Each chapter of part I deals with one category, giving some guidance
on how to go about answering such questions. There is a discussion and
one or more worked examples, followed by an exercise. All this has been
written with the young learner in mind. You are encouraged to make a
serious attempt at each problem in these exercises (and to do so before
looking at the solution).

Part II

Each chapter in part II contains basic 'Facts' that can be used to explain
a solution. You may already know many of these, but even if you do it
is useful to gather them all together, not least because then the authors
can refer to them consistently. These chapters also discuss some of the
methods of solution that you ought to be aware of.

Solutions

Solutions—not just answers—to all the problems in the exercises are given
in appendix A. These are not the same as those provided each year in the
JMO solutions booklet: usually the solutions here are much fuller and
hopefully clarify how you might write down your thoughts when you
tackle a problem.

---

[*] In a few cases the wording or layout of a question has been slightly altered.

In many cases a problem has more than one method of solution. You may find a solution which you think is better than any of those given here, or you may find one which you prefer for other reasons. Be reassured: any valid solution, well presented, will receive full credit in an Olympiad. And the ability to discover a different solution is a good indicator that you have the potential to do well.

Of course, the solutions in this book do not show any 'rough work' and on the whole tend not to discuss methods which fail. Often a lot of work has gone into understanding a problem and its solution before even thinking about writing out a solution, and none of this work is shown.

Occasionally we give a commentary on a solution. These remarks are not part of what is needed in a full written solution so can safely be ignored, but they may help you to understand why we have done something. Try reading them if you are puzzled, or if you just want to learn more about how to solve problems.

1.2   Using the book

We suggest that you start by having a go at a few of the problems in part I and build up from there. You may wish to choose a type of problem that you enjoy solving rather than something completely unfamiliar, and you may like to try the first one or two problems in an exercise. (Note that problems of the same type are gathered together in exercises, and the problems get harder as you pass through an exercise.)

Clearly, it would not be a good idea to start with a chapter which has the word 'more' in the title; that can wait till later.

You are strongly advised to try the questions first before looking at the solutions.

Give yourself time, use paper and pencil, and make a determined effort to solve each problem in your own way. Only after you have found your own method, or when you really need some help, should you turn to the solution given here. But then you will have a better understanding of the problem, and so will be able to appreciate the solution much more.

You may wish to glance briefly at the guidance in chapter 2 before you start the problems, then come back to it later as you need.

If you are about to enter the JMO, then you may find chapter 3 helpful.

You may occasionally come across a new word, or forget the meaning of an old one. In either case, you should try looking up the word in the glossary or in the index.

Part II is for reference: you will find that we continually refer to facts in part II; you may wish to refer to it as you go along.

When faced with unusual or challenging problems, what you need above all is perseverance, the desire to keep trying until some progress is made. Take your time when trying a problem and keep puzzling away until it yields up its secrets. Success is rarely a question of extra knowledge, more often one of know-how.

This book is full of guidance, but the best preparation is practice, and there are plenty of questions for you to try. The guidance given in each section should help you to attempt the problems in the exercises. Remember, you should only refer to the solutions when you have succeeded in finding a solution yourself, or if you make little progress after spending some time thinking about the problem.

Chapter 2

General guidance

> If you can't solve a problem, then there is an easier problem you can solve: find it.
>
> George Pólya
> *How to solve it*

2.1 Writing solutions

The chapters of this book contain a lot of guidance about how to write out your solution to a problem. Nevertheless, you may find the following additional general points helpful.

✳ You should not aim to write a polished solution. What you should do is set out the steps in your solution in a clear and logical manner, so that anyone reading your work can readily follow your mathematical argument.

✳ It is helpful to lay out your solution line-by-line, with each new assertion beginning on a new line. You should also remember to include clear diagrams where necessary; it is better to have too many diagrams than too few.

✳ Do not expect anyone reading your solution to do your work for you, which means that you should carefully present complete calculations. For example, if you are looking at cases, then you should give detailed working for each of them.

* Try not to make claims without explanation. For example, you might say "$\angle FDG = 60°$". On its own this is not helpful, because you have not explained *why* the angle is that size.

* Finally, you should be aware that answers obtained by inexact methods deserve little credit. For that reason you should avoid approaches like scale drawing. Similarly, calculations which involve converting exact numbers such as π, $\sqrt{2}$ or even $\frac{1}{3}$ to approximate decimals like 3.14, 1.414 or 0.33 are also wasted effort.

2.2　Strategy

Solutions are more than just answers, and finding the answer is not as important as finding an overall strategy to solve a problem—a way to plan a route to a solution.

You should appreciate that looking at something in general is much more efficient than considering individual cases, because then you can be sure you have not left out some answers, and have not included any which are incorrect.

Don't stop

When you have found an answer, you should not stop, but should make certain that there are no other possible answers. In some cases, your method will ensure that the answer you have found is the only one and that there are no others. In many cases, you should add an argument to explain why there are no other answers.

So you should clearly show that you have considered any other answers and that they are impossible. Many candidates are unsuccessful because they find an answer and think that must be the only answer. This may be the case, but often it is not.

Trial and error

You should not use trial and error when solving problems of this kind. Apart from anything else, if you do, then it is difficult to be certain that you have considered all possible cases.

The method of 'trial and improvement' may sometimes be useful to find approximate solutions to equations, but is usually not appropriate for Olympiad questions.

Listing

You should only attempt to list all possibilities when there are just a few cases to deal with. Then you need to be systematic and to show all your working, since you need to convince anyone reading your work that your list is complete and does not include any duplicates. An example is given in section 19.1.

2.3 Checking

Wherever possible, you should check that any numerical answers you have found actually do fit the question. This is such good practice that it is worth developing as a matter of habit. When you carry out such a check, write down some details of what you have done.

On some occasions it is not possible to check a numerical answer to a question (some of the later problems in this book are like this). Consider, say, a geometrical proof, where the only things that you can check are the logic of your argument and whether you have used relevant facts. Nevertheless, neither of these is insignificant; it is just difficult to write down how they have been checked. So you should always attempt a check.

Chapter 3

The Junior Mathematical Olympiad

The Junior Mathematical Olympiad (JMO) was introduced in 1989 to provide young mathematicans with an opportunity to experience challenging mathematics not generally met in school. The JMO has since become an annual event. Approximately 1000 pupils are invited to participate, and are thereby given the chance to have the thrill and satisfaction of solving interesting and unfamiliar problems.

The setters of the problems attempt to pose questions which are readily understood yet require some insight beyond the confines of a school syllabus. Another aim is to instill an awareness of the need to write clear, precise, logical and structured solutions. Rather than the answer itself, emphasis is placed on the chain of reasoning which leads to that answer.

It is also hoped that, in solving a sophisticated problem, you will gain enjoyment and a wish to tackle even more challenging questions. The problems are not routine, yet the alert candidate should be able to solve them using known skills. Nevertheless, you should expect the unexpected!

At the time of writing, the actual Olympiad paper has two parts.

Section A consists of ten short, answer-only questions.

Section B contains six questions of increasing difficulty, for which full written solutions are required.

The time allocated for the Olympiad paper is 2 hours, which in itself provides a challenge. You should be aware that section B questions gain more marks than those in section A and allocate the time you spend on them carefully. Also, if you successfully complete three or four section B questions, then you will have done well.

3.1   Section A

The questions in section A of the JMO are significantly different from those in section B. They require only an answer, and no explanation or proof needs to be given. Each question is worth one mark, making a total of 10 for section A. It is therefore wise to use your time carefully and not spent too much time on Part A. Although your final mark depends on both sections, section B plays a much more important role in determining your total score.

There is no further reference in this book to section A.

3.2   Section B

Few candidates will do all the problems in section B of the paper and doing three or four fully is exceptional. You should aim to solve one or two questions first, then if time allows go on to others. The early problems tend to be easier, the later ones harder, so it is fairly clear where to start!

Do not be afraid of spending time on one question, doing a lot of rough work, and trying different approaches. But do remember to allow time to write out your solution to each question in a clearly explained way. Few marks are awarded whenever a candidate just hands in an 'answer', or a jumble of rough working. Indeed, you are instructed *not* to hand in rough working.

You are being encouraged to think outside your comfort zone—going beyond the normal set of rules and techniques learned in school—so there are a few things that you should remember.

* You will gain more marks by completing a whole question rather than giving incomplete solutions to several questions.

* You should read each question carefully and think before you put pen to paper. As part of this thinking process, try to build up an idea about how you might answer the question and then develop this idea towards a solution.

✳ When a question is given in parts, one part is often a clue to how you might go about solving the next part.

Notice that section B marks are awarded in 'Olympiad' fashion, which is probably very different from anything you are used to. Under this system, you may gain only 1 or 2 marks (out of 10) even when you have the correct answer. High marks can only be achieved when the written solution is almost complete.

In particular, notice that an answer is not enough by itself. A solution requires an explanation of every step in your thinking. You will see when you read the solutions provided in this book that you are expected to explain any claim you make.

For example, suppose you wish to solve the following problem.

Four children with different hair colour are chosen from three blondes, four redheads, seven with auburn hair and nine with black hair. In how many different ways can they be selected?

On its own, the correct answer 756 would only gain 1 mark. It is not worth much because if this is all you tell someone who wants to know the answer, they have to take it on trust that you have used a correct method and have not made a numerical mistake. Also, the answer, by itself, does not give any clue as to how to solve a similar problem with different numbers.

To gain high marks you need in addition to give an argument to justify your claim that 756 is the correct answer. (This is good practice anyway since you may make a slip in the arithmetic and so arrive at the wrong answer, but would gain a lot of credit for explaining a correct method.)

The markers usually award 1, 2 or 3 for an incomplete solution, and 7, 8, 9 or 10 for an almost complete, or complete, solution.

Part I

Problems

Chapter 4

Introducing letters

Example

The diagram below is to be completed so that:

(i) each box contains a positive integer;
(ii) the total of the numbers in the thirteen boxes is 2005; and
(iii) the sum of the numbers in any three consecutive boxes is always the same.

	175										70	

In how many different ways is it possible to complete the diagram in this way?

Discussion

The question deals with the sum of whole numbers, that is, positive integers. The question also refers to consecutive boxes, which means adjacent boxes.

We shall introduce a letter to represent the unknown integer in one of the boxes. Let a represent the integer in the first box.

We still have no way of building an equation to describe the situation. We need to introduce a second letter for the unknown integer in another of the boxes, and we have a choice: either we can let the second unknown represent the sum of the integers in three consecutive boxes, or we can let the second unknown represent the integer in some other box. We shall choose the latter method since then we only need to use addition facts.

However, we still have a choice: the second unknown can represent the number in the third box (the next empty one), the fourth box, or indeed in any other empty box. The approach we use below is probably the simplest.

The problem asks 'how many different ways ...?' so be sure to give an answer to that question.

Solution

Let a and b represent the integers on either side of 175.

The sum of the numbers in the first three boxes is $a + 175 + b$. Since the second and third boxes contain 175 and b, condition (iii) forces the fourth box to contain a. Always considering three adjacent boxes in this way, we may work along the row of boxes and fill them in as shown:

a	175	b	a	175	b	a	175	b	a	175	b	a

By comparing with the diagram given in the question, we therefore see that $b = 70$. So the integers in the boxes are:

a	175	70	a	175	70	a	175	70	a	175	70	a

Applying condition (ii), we obtain

$$5a + 4 \times 175 + 4 \times 70 = 2005,$$

and so

$$5a + 700 + 280 = 2005,$$

that is,

$$5a + 980 = 2005.$$

Subtracting 980 from each side, we obtain

$$5a = 2005 - 980$$
$$= 1025.$$

and so, dividing both sides by 5, we get

$$a = 205.$$

Therefore there is exactly one way of completing the diagram:

205	175	70	205	175	70	205	175	70	205	175	70	205

CHECK   The numbers in the boxes are all integers, which meets condition (i). Any three consecutive boxes contain the integers 205, 175 and 70 (in some order) and so condition (iii) is met. The total in the thirteen boxes is $205 + 175 + 70 + 205 + 175 + 70 + 205 + 175 + 70 + 205 + 175 + 70 + 205 = 2005$ and hence condition (ii) is also satisfied.

REMARK   Our method also shows that these are the *only* values that work.

Exercise 4

B1 **1.** Kate has 90 identical blocks. She uses all of the blocks to build this four-step 'staircase' in which each step, apart from the top one, has the same length.

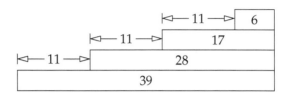

(a) Show that there are exactly two different ways in which it is possible to use all of the 90 blocks to build a six-step 'staircase'.

(b) Explain why it is impossible to use all 90 blocks to build a seven-step 'staircase'.

B1 **2.** In her purse, Jenny has 20 coins, with a total value of £5. There are three denominations of coin—10p, 20p and 50p—in her purse and she has more 50p coins than 10p coins.

How many of each type of coin does she have?

B1 **3.** Find four integers whose sum is 400 and such that the first integer is equal to twice the second integer, three times the third integer and four times the fourth integer.

B1 **4.** In 2007 Alphonse grew twice the number of grapes that Pierre did. In 2008 Pierre grew twice the number of grapes that Alphonse did. Over the two years Alphonse grew 49 000 grapes, which was 7600 less than Pierre.

How many grapes did Alphonse grow in 2007?

B1 **5.** In a sequence of six numbers, every term after the second term is the sum of the previous two terms. Also, the last term is four times the first term, and the sum of all six terms is 13.

What is the first term?

B1 **6.** There was an old woman who lived in a shoe. She had 9 children at regular intervals of 15 months. The oldest is now six times as old as the youngest.

How old is the youngest child?

B1 **7.** How many numbers less than 2013 are both:
  (i) the sum of two consecutive positive integers; and
  (ii) the sum of five consecutive positive integers?

B2 **8.** The diagram shows a square which has been divided into five congruent rectangles. The perimeter of each rectangle is 51 cm.

What is the perimeter of the square?

B2 **9.** A 3×3 grid contains nine numbers, not necessarily integers, one in each cell. Each number is doubled to obtain the number on its immediate right and trebled to obtain the number immediately below it.

If the sum of the nine numbers is 13, what is the value of the number in the central cell?

B2 **10.** Three identical rectangular cards can be placed end to end (with their short sides touching) to make rectangle A, and can be placed side by side (with their long sides touching) to make rectangle B. The perimeter of rectangle A is twice the perimeter of rectangle B.

Find the ratio of the length of a short side to the length of a long side of each card.

Chapter 5

Angles and lines

Example

In the figure, ADC is a straight line and $AB = BC = CD$. Also, $DA = DB$.

Find the size of $\angle CAB$.

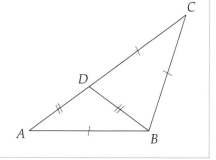

Discussion

Notice that we can find three different triangles in this diagram. You may find it useful to deal with each of these triangles separately as you work through your solution.

There are several pairs of sides of equal length and this encourages us to look for special triangles which do have equal sides (isosceles or equilateral triangles).

When you are trying to find the size of an angle, it is often a good idea to represent this by an unknown, that is, to introduce a letter and then use some algebra.

Remember that it is also essential to give a reason in words for each step of your argument.

Solution

Let $\angle CAB$ be $x°$ (see the figure).

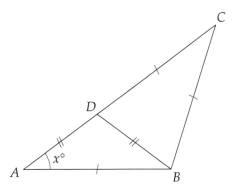

Consider the triangle BDA. We have $BD = DA$ and so triangle BDA is isosceles. Therefore $\angle ABD = \angle DAB = x°$ because *the angles opposite equal sides of a triangle are equal.*

Applying *the exterior angle of a triangle is equal to the sum of the two interior opposite angles* to triangle BDA, we have $\angle CDB = \angle DAB + \angle ABD$, which is $x° + x° = 2x°$.

Now consider the triangle BCD. We have $BC = CD$ and so triangle BCD is isosceles. Therefore $\angle DBC = \angle CDB$ because *the angles opposite equal sides of a triangle are equal,* so that $\angle DBC = 2x°$.

Applying *the sum of the angles in a triangle is 180°* to triangle BCD, we have

$$\angle BCD + \angle CDB + \angle DBC = 180°$$

and so

$$\angle BCD + 2x° + 2x° = 180°.$$

Therefore we have

$$\angle BCD + 4x° = 180°$$

and, subtracting $4x°$ from each side, we get

$$\angle BCD = 180° - 4x°.$$

Fac
17.4
p 1C
Fac
17.4
p 1C

Fac
17.4
p 1C

Fac
17.4
p 1C
Fac
17.4
p 1C

Fact
7.4D
▸107

Finally, the triangle ABC is isosceles with $AB = BC$. Therefore $\angle BCA = \angle CAB$, once again because *the angles opposite equal sides of a triangle are equal.*

Hence

$$x = 180 - 4x,$$

and adding $4x$ to each side, we get

$$5x = 180.$$

Now dividing each side by 5, we obtain

$$x = 36.$$

Therefore $\angle CAB = 36°$.

CHECK Notice that when $x = 36°$ we can calculate all the angles, as shown in the following figure.

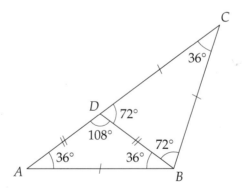

All three triangles are, indeed, isosceles, as given in the question.

REMARK On its own, this last diagram does *not* provide a solution to the question, because it does not show why there are no other values that work. In any case, no reasons are given for the calculations.

Exercise 5

B2 **1.** *AOC* is a straight line and angle *BOA* = 42°.

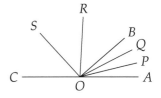

OP and OQ trisect angle *BOA* (which means they divide the angle into three equal parts).

OR and OS trisect angle *COB*.

   (a) Showing all working, calculate angle *ROQ* and angle *SOP*.

   (b) Calculate angle *ROQ* when angle *BOA* = *x*°.

B2 **2.** *ABCD* is a square. The point *E* is outside the square so that *CDE* is an equilateral triangle.

Find angle *BED*.

B2 **3.** The diagram shows triangle *ABC*, in which ∠*ABC* = 72° and ∠*CAB* = 84°. The point *E* lies on *AB* so that *EC* bisects ∠*BCA*. The point *F* lies on *CA* extended. The point *D* lies on *CB* extended so that *DA* bisects ∠*BAF*.

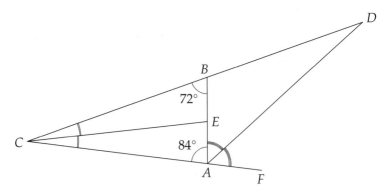

Prove that *AD* = *CE*.

B3 **4.** The diagram shows an equlateral triangle inside a rhombus. The sides of the rhombus are equal in length to the sides of the triangle.

What is the value of x?

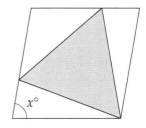

B3 **5.** In the diagram, B is the midpoint of AC and the lines AP, BQ and CR are parallel. The bisector of $\angle PAB$ meets BQ at Z. Draw a diagram to show this, and join Z to C.

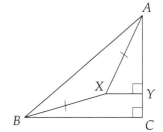

    (a) Given that $\angle PAZ = x°$, find $\angle ZBC$ in terms of x.

    (b) Show that CZ bisects $\angle BCR$.

(You must give full reasons to justify your answers.)

B3 **6.** In the diagram, Y lies on the line AC, triangles ABC and AXY are right-angled, and in triangle ABX, $AX = BX$. The line segment AX bisects angle BAC and angle AXY is seven times the size of angle XBC.

What is the size of angle ABC?

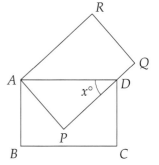

B3 **7.** In the diagram $ABCD$ and $APQR$ are congruent rectangles.

The side PQ passes through the point D and $\angle PDA = x°$.

Find an expression for $\angle QRD$ in terms of x.

B4 **8.** In a triangle ABC, the point M lies on AC and N lies on AB so that
$\angle BNC = 4x°$, $\angle BCN = 6x°$ and $\angle BMC = \angle CBM = 5x°$.

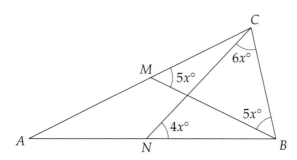

Prove that triangle ABC is isosceles.

Chapter 6

Arithmetic

Example

> In a sequence, each term after the first is the sum of the squares of the digits of the previous term. Thus, if the first term were 12, the second term would be $1^2 + 2^2 = 5$, the third term $5^2 = 25$, the fourth term $2^2 + 5^2 = 29$ and so on.
>
> (a) Find the first five terms of the sequence whose first term is 25.
>
> (b) Find the 2001st term of the sequence whose first term is 25.

Discussion

Clearly we cannot be expected to answer part (b) by calculating all of the first 2001 terms of the sequence. Instead we need to find a pattern in the sequence.

In this type of question, ensure that you do not suggest that the sequence repeats itself without *proving* that this is so. An explanation of why the sequence continues in a cycle for ever is required.

Solution

(a) Applying the rule, we obtain:

$$\text{first term} = 25;$$

$$\text{second term} = 2^2 + 5^2$$
$$= 29;$$
$$\text{third term} = 2^2 + 9^2$$
$$= 85;$$
$$\text{fourth term} = 8^2 + 5^2$$
$$= 89;$$
$$\text{and fifth term} = 8^2 + 9^2$$
$$= 145.$$

So the first five terms of the sequence are 25, 29, 85, 89 and 145.

(b) Continuing, we get:

$$\text{sixth term} = 1^2 + 4^2 + 5^2$$
$$= 42;$$
$$\text{seventh term} = 4^2 + 2^2$$
$$= 20;$$
$$\text{eighth term} = 2^2 + 0^2$$
$$= 4;$$
$$\text{ninth term} = 4^2$$
$$= 16;$$
$$\text{tenth term} = 1^2 + 6^2$$
$$= 37;$$
$$\text{eleventh term} = 3^2 + 7^2$$
$$= 58;$$
$$\text{and twelfth term} = 5^2 + 8^2$$
$$= 89.$$

Now we notice that 89 appeared earlier in the sequence and so the sequence will repeat: future terms will follow in the same order because the same calculations are involved. It is important here to do more than observe that a finite number of terms of the sequence repeats—which is just spotting a pattern—it is essential to explain how we know that the sequence will repeat *for ever*.

The sequence is 25, 29, 85, **89**, 145 , 42, 20, 4, 16, 37, 58, **89**, 145, 42, 20, 4, 16, ... There are three terms at the start, then there is a repeating cycle of eight terms.

Now

$$2001 = 3 + 1998$$
$$= 3 + (249 \times 8 + 6)$$

and so the required integer is the sixth number in the repeating cycle, which is 16.

Example

> Marisa and Andrew travel from Glasgow to Motherwell. Marisa travels the first half of the route at 6 mph and the remainder at 12 mph. She takes a total time of x hours.
>
> Andrew travels the first third of the route at 5 mph and the remainder at 15 mph. He takes a total time of y hours to complete the journey.
>
> What is the ratio $x : y$?

Discussion

Remember that there are three results connecting the distance travelled, the time taken and the speed of travel:

act
.8A
.95

$$speed = \frac{distance}{time}; \ time = \frac{distance}{speed}; \ distance = speed \times time.$$

act
.8C
.95

Which do we choose to use here? Since the results are all equivalent—any of them may be obtained from the others—it does not really matter, but we select the one that is most convenient. We are asked to find a ratio of times taken, whereas the speeds are given and the distance is always the same, so we shall use

act
.8B
.95

$$time = \frac{distance}{speed}.$$

Though the solution that follows appears to use algebra—we introduce a letter—it is really about fractions. Even so, it is vital that any letters we do use are chosen wisely and described clearly. Since the question gives some speeds and refers to the times x hours and y hours, we introduce a letter for the *distance*.

Twice in the solution we add two fractions together. To do so we make use of a *common denominator*, that is, we change each fraction so that it has the same number on the bottom.

Solution

Let the distance travelled from Glasgow to Motherwell be d miles.

Consider the first half of Marisa's journey. She covers a distance of $\frac{1}{2}d$ miles at a speed of 6 mph. Using the fact that

$$time = \frac{distance}{speed},$$

Fac
15.8
p 95

we find that the time in hours for the first part of Marisa's journey equals

$$\frac{\frac{1}{2}d}{6} = \frac{d}{12}.$$

In the same way, the time in hours for the second part of Marisa's journey equals

$$\frac{\frac{1}{2}d}{12} = \frac{d}{24}.$$

The total number of hours for Marisa's journey is therefore equal to

$$\frac{d}{12} + \frac{d}{24} = \frac{2d}{24} + \frac{d}{24}$$
$$= \frac{3d}{24}$$
$$= \frac{d}{8}.$$

Now consider the first third of Andrew's journey. He covers a distance of $\frac{1}{3}d$ at a speed of 5 mph. It follows that the time in hours for the first part of Andrew's journey equals

$$\frac{\frac{1}{3}d}{5} = \frac{d}{15}.$$

In the same way, the time in hours for the second part of Andrew's journey equals

$$\frac{\frac{2}{3}d}{15} = \frac{2d}{45}.$$

The total time in hours for Andrew's journey is therefore equal to

$$\frac{d}{15} + \frac{2d}{45} = \frac{3d}{45} + \frac{2d}{45}$$

$$= \frac{5d}{45}$$

$$= \frac{d}{9}.$$

Hence the ratio $x : y$ is equal to $\dfrac{d}{8} : \dfrac{d}{9}$.

We could stop there, but there are two difficulties in doing so: the answer involves d, an unknown that *we* introduced; the ratio has a simpler form.

We can deal with the first difficulty by dividing both terms by d, to obtain

$$x : y = \frac{1}{8} : \frac{1}{9}.$$

Now, writing each fraction in a form with denominator 72, we get

$$x : y = \frac{9}{72} : \frac{8}{72}$$

$$= 9 : 8.$$

REMARK   It is essential that you remember to answer the actual question that is being asked. Giving an answer as a fraction here is unlikely to be considered a complete solution.

Exercise 6

B1 **1.** Find all of the ways in which 200 can be written in the form $p + q^2 + r^3$ where p, q and r are prime numbers.

B1 **2.** The first three terms of a sequence are $\frac{1}{4}$, $\frac{1}{3}$, $\frac{1}{2}$. The fourth term is $\frac{1}{2} - \frac{1}{3} + \frac{1}{4}$; henceforth, each new term is calculated by taking the previous term, subtracting the term before that, and then adding the term before that.

    (a) Write down the first six terms of the sequence, giving your answers as simplified fractions.

    (b) Find the 10th term and the 100th term, and explain why they have to be what you claim.

B1 **3.** Let N be the smallest positive integer whose digits add up to 2015.

    What is the sum of the digits of $N + 1$?

B2 **4.** A crossnumber puzzle is like a crossword puzzle, except that the answers are numbers instead of words and each square contains one single digit. None of the answers starts with the digit 0.

ACROSS	DOWN
1. A square.	1. A cube.
3. A square.	2. A square.
4. A square.	3. A cube times a square.

How many solutions are there to this crossnumber?

B2 **5.** Each of the whole numbers from 1 to 10 is to be placed in the circles so that the sum of each line of three numbers is equal to T. Four numbers have already been entered.

Find all the possible values of T.

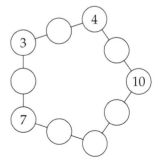

B3 **6.** The solution to each clue of this crossnumber is a two-digit number. None of these numbers begins with zero.

ACROSS	DOWN
1. A multiple of 3.	1. A multiple of 25.
3. Three times a prime.	2. A square.

Complete the crossnumber, stating the order in which you solved the clues and explaining why there is only one possibility at each stage.

B3 **7.** (a) Yesterday evening, my journey home took 25% longer than usual. By what percentage was my average speed reduced compared to normal?

(b) By what percentage would I need to increase my usual average speed in order for the journey to take 20% less time than usual?

B3 **8.** Tom left a motorway service station and travelled towards Glasgow at a steady speed of 60 mph. Tim left the same service station 10 minutes after Tom and travelled in the same direction at a steady speed, overtaking Tom after a further 1 hour 40 minutes.

At what speed did Tim travel?

B4 **9.** How many different solutions are there to the letter sum on the right?

Different letters stand for different digits, and no number begins with zero.

$$\begin{array}{r} J\,M\,C \\ +\ J\,M\,O \\ \hline S\,U\,M\,S \end{array}$$

B4 **10.** The solution to each clue of this crossnumber is a two-digit positive integer, not beginning with zero.

ACROSS	DOWN
1. A triangular number.	1. A square.
3. A triangular number.	2. A multiple of 5.

In how many different ways can the crossnumber be completed correctly?

Chapter 7

Divisibility

Example

The eight-digit integer '$ppppqqqq$', where p and q are digits, is a multiple of 45.

What are the possible values of p?

Discussion

If you look ahead to section 15.3 on page 88 you will see that we only note divisibility facts for small integers. Therefore, a good start here is to use the prime factorisation theorem for 45, in order to see which small integers we actually need to consider.

Also, the number in the question is a very large integer, in the tens of millions, and so we are really only interested in p and q rather than the actual integer itself.

In examples such as these, it is important that you check that any answer that you find actually does fit the requirements of the question. It is easy when working in the abstract to make a logical error and come up with false answers.

Solution

Now $45 = 3^2 \times 5$, so that an integer is divisible by 45 when it is both divisible by $3^2 = 9$ and divisible by 5, and not otherwise, from the fact that *an integer is divisible by an integer n when it is divisible by the highest power of each prime in the prime factorisation of n, and not otherwise.*

Fact 15.3 p91

The integer is divisible by 5 and so the final digit is 5 or 0, using the fact that *an integer is divisible by 5 when the last digit is 0 or 5, and not otherwise.* Therefore $q = 0$ or $q = 5$.

Fact 15.3 p89

The integer is also divisible by 9. Let us consider each of these values of q in turn, using the fact that *an integer is divisible by 9 when the sum of the digits is divisible by 9, and not otherwise.*

Fact 15.3 p89

$q = 0$

The sum of the digits of '$pp\,pp0\,000$' is $4 \times p$, so we require $4p$ to be divisible by 9.

Remembering that p is a single digit and can only take integer values between 0 and 9, it follows that $4p$ is 0, 4, 8, 12, 16, 20, 24, 28, 32 or 36. It is clear that only one of these, 36, is divisible by 9.

Therefore $p = 9$, in which case the integer is $99\,990\,000$.

$q = 5$

The sum of the digits of '$pp\,pp5\,555$' is $4p + 20$. We require $4p + 20$ to be divisible by 9.

Remembering that p is a single digit and can only take integer values between 0 and 9, it follows that $4p + 20$ is 20, 24, 28, 32, 36, 40, 44, 48, 52 or 56. From this list, only 36 is divisible by 9. This gives $4p + 20 = 36$, so that $4p = 16$

Therefore $p = 4$, in which case the integer is $44\,445\,555$.

Hence the possible values of p are 4 and 9.

CHECK $44\,445\,555 = 45 \times 987\,678$ and $99\,990\,000 = 45 \times 2\,222\,000$, so that these two eight-digit integers do indeed satisfy the given conditions.

REMARK   Our method also shows that these are the *only* integers that work.

Exercise 7

B1 **1.** Suppose you know that the middle two digits of a four-digit integer N are '12' in that order and that N is an exact multiple of 15.

Determine all the different possibilities for the integer N.

(You must explain clearly why your list is complete.)

B1 **2.** Every digit of a given positive integer is either a 3 or a 4 with each occurring at least once. The integer is divisible by both 3 and 4.

What is the smallest such integer?

B2 **3.** Anastasia thinks of a positive integer, which Barry then doubles. Next, Charlie trebles Barry's number. Finally, Damion multiplies Charlie's number by six. Eve notices that the sum of these four numbers is a perfect square.

What is the smallest number that Anastasia could have thought of?

B4 **4.** Find a rule which predicts exactly when five consecutive integers have sum divisible by 15.

B5 **5.** (a) Explain why the sum of three consecutive integers is always divisible by three.

(b) Is it true that the sum of four consecutive integers is always divisible by 4?

(c) For which k is it true that the sum of k consecutive integers is always divisible by k?

B5 **6.** Consider three-digit integers N with the two properties:

(i) N is not exactly divisible by 2, 3 or 5;
(ii) no digit of N is exactly divisible by 2, 3 or 5.

How many such integers N are there?

B5 **7.** Find a fraction $\dfrac{m}{n}$, where m and n are different positive integers , such that all of the fractions

$$\frac{m}{n}, \ \frac{m+1}{n+1}, \ \frac{m+2}{n+2}, \ \frac{m+3}{n+3}, \ \frac{m+4}{n+4}, \ \frac{m+5}{n+5}$$

can be simplified by cancelling.

Chapter 8

How many ways?

Example

An irregular pentagon has five different interior angles each of which measures an integer number of degrees. One angle is 76°. The other four angles are three-digit integers which fit one digit per cell across and down into the grid on the right.

In how many different ways can the grid be completed?

Discussion

Notice that this is a multistage problem involving different areas of mathematics. In such a case, work carefully through each part separately rather than attempt to do everything together.

This question has three different parts: geometry and angles, a cross-number, and then counting the number of possible solutions. There is a fairly simple geometric start in finding the total of the four required angles. The problem is then greatly simplified in that each of the possible-three digit integers starts with the digit 1. Then, as usual, the use of algebra by way of introducing letters for the unknowns reduces the amount of work which needs to be done.

You will score very few marks for finding a few values which work. The major part of this question is the 'how many ways' part and thinking about the number of choices of digits—as shown on page 86—is a very efficient way of producing a complete solution.

Solution

Using *the sum of the interior angles of a polygon with n sides is* $(n-2) \times 180°$, we know that the sum of the angles in a pentagon is $3 \times 180° = 540°$. Therefore the total of the four missing three-digit integers is $540 - 76 = 464$.

Fac
17.5
p 11

The first digit of each of the four three-digit integers can only be 1, otherwise the total would have a digit greater than 4 in the 'hundreds' column.

Let the digits in the missing cells be a, b, c, d and y, as indicated in the following figure, so the four integers are '$1a1$', '$1b1$', '$1cy$' and '$1dy$'.

1	a	1
b		c
1	d	y

The total of the four integers is 464, so that their units digits add up to an 4 or to 14 since the largest possible 'carry' is 1. Hence $1 + 1 + y + y = 4$ or $1 + 1 + y + y = 14$, and the only possible values of y are 1 and 6. We shall deal with each case in turn.

$y = 1$

1	a	1
b		c
1	d	1

The four integers are '$1a1$', '$1b1$', '$1c1$' and '$1d1$'. But their total is 464, so that $a + b + c + d = 6$. However, the four integers are different, and so a, b, c and d are different. The only possibility is for a, b, c and d to be equal to 0, 1, 2 and 3 in some order.

Consider how a, b, c and d can be chosen. There are 4 ways of choosing a, leaving 3 choices for b and 2 choices for c. Once the other three integers have been chosen, d is fixed with only one possible choice.

Altogether, there are $4 \times 3 \times 2 \times 1 = 24$ ways of placing the digits 0, 1, 2 and 3, using *the multiplication principle*. So in this case there are 24 ways of completing the grid.

Fact
9.1A
121

$y = 6$

1	a	1
b		c
1	d	6

The four integers are '$1a1$', '$1b1$', '$1c6$' and '$1d6$'. But their total is 464, so that $a + b + c + d = 5$. However, the four integers are different, and so a and b are different, and c and d are different. The only possibilities are for a, b, c and d to equal (in some order) 0, 0, 1 and 4, or 0, 0, 2 and 3, or 0, 1, 1 and 3, or 0, 1, 2 and 2. Thus there are 4 possible selections of the four digits.

How may each of these selections be placed in the grid? Notice that in each selection two of the digits are equal. There are four ways to place this pair of equal digits: a and c; a and d; b and c; and b and d. Once this pair of digits has been placed, the remaining two digits may be placed in 2×1 ways. So there are $4 \times 2 \times 1 = 8$ ways of placing each selection, using *the multiplication principle*.

act
.1A
121

There are 4 selections, each of which may be placed in 8 ways, so in this case there are $4 \times 8 = 32$ ways of completing the grid.

Hence there are $24 + 32 = 56$ ways altogether in which the grid may be completed.

Exercise 8

B1 **1.** The numbers from 1 to 7 inclusive are to be placed, one per square, in the diagram on the right so that the totals of the three numbers in the horizontal row and each of the two columns are the same.

In how many different ways can this be done if the numbers 1 and 2 must be in the positions shown?

B1 **2.** A number like 4679 is called an *ascending* number because each digit in the number is larger than the preceding one.

    (a) How many ascending numbers are there between 1000 and 2000?

    (b) How many ascending numbers are there between 1000 and 10 000?

B2 **3.** I start at the square marked A and make a succession of moves to the square marked B. Each move may only be made downward or to the right. I take the sum of all the numbers in my path and add 5 for every grey square I pass through.

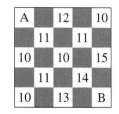

How many paths give a sum of 51?

B3 **4.** Jack starts in the small square shown shaded on the grid, and makes a sequence of moves. Each move is to a neighbouring small square, where two small squares are neighbouring if they have an edge in common. He may visit a square more than once.

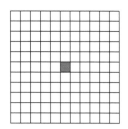

Jack makes four moves. In how many different small squares could Jack finish?

B4 **5.** (a) Find the sum of all positive three-digit integers each of whose digits is either 2 or 3.

(b) Find the sum of all positive six-digit integers each of whose digits is either 2 or 3, giving your answer as the product of prime numbers.

Chapter 9

More integers

Example

Observe that $49 = 4 \times 9 + 4 + 9$.

(a) Find all other two-digit positive integers which are equal to the product of their digits plus the sum of their digits.

(b) Prove that there are no three-digit positive integers which are equal to the product of their digits plus the sum of their digits.

Discussion

When answering questions of this type, remember that the way to write a general two-digit integer is to use the expression 'ab', which is used to mean the two-digit integer with value $10 \times a + b$. Note the use of quotation marks to distinguish the notation from ab, which means $a \times b$.

You need to read such questions carefully—it is important to be aware what type of numbers you are dealing with: are they whole numbers, or positive integers, or . . . .

Part (b) is essentially asking us to prove something is impossible. See section 19.3 on page 125.

Solution

(a) Let the two-digit integer be '*ab*'. Notice that '*ab*' is $10a + b$ in the decimal number system.

Then, from the information given in the question, we have

$$10a + b = a \times b + a + b$$

so that, subtracting $a + b$ from each side,

$$9a = ab.$$

Dividing both sides by a (we may do this because a is not zero), we obtain

$$9 = b.$$

Therefore there are eight other two-digit integers which satisfy the condition, namely 19, 29, 39, 59, 69, 79, 89 and 99.

CHECK $19 = 1 \times 9 + 1 + 9$; $29 = 2 \times 9 + 2 + 9$; $39 = 3 \times 9 + 3 + 9$; $59 = 5 \times 9 + 5 + 9$; $69 = 6 \times 9 + 6 + 9$; $79 = 7 \times 9 + 7 + 9$; $89 = 8 \times 9 + 8 + 9$; and $99 = 9 \times 9 + 9 + 9$. So all these two-digit integers satisfy the given conditions.

REMARK   Our method also shows that these are the *only* values that work.

(b) Let the three-digit integer be '*abc*', which is $100a + 10b + c$ in the decimal number system.

Then, from the information given in the question, we have

$$100a + 10b + c = abc + a + b + c$$

so that, subtracting $a + b + c$ from each side, we have

$$99a + 9b = abc,$$

and then subtracting $99a$ from each side,

$$9b = abc - 99a. \tag{*}$$

The largest value that each of b and c can take is 9. Hence the largest value of abc is $81a$. Therefore the largest value of $abc - 99a$ is $-18a$, which is always negative (since a is not zero). Thus the right-hand side of equation (*) is always negative, whereas the left-hand side is positive or zero, which is impossible.

Therefore there are no three-digit integers with the required property.

Exercise 9

B4 **1.** The diagram shows a large rectangle whose perimeter is 300 cm. It is divided up as shown into a number of identical rectangles, each of perimeter 58 cm. Each side of these rectangles is a whole number of centimetres.

Show that there are exactly two possibilities for the number of smaller rectangles and find the size of the large rectangle in each case.

B5 **2.** (a) Find all two-digit positive integers which are increased by 75% when their digits are reversed.

    (b) Find all three-digit positive integers which are increased by 75% when their digits are reversed.

B5 **3.** In a magic hexagram, the numbers in every line of four circles have the same total. The diagram shows a magic hexagram which uses twelve different prime numbers.

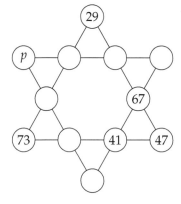

Five numbers are shown, including the smallest and the largest of the twelve primes.

Find the value of p, explaining the steps in your reasoning.

B5 **4.** I have two types of square tile. One type has a side length of 1 cm and the other has a side length of 2 cm.

What is the smallest square that can be made with equal numbers of each type of tile?

B6 **5.** 12 is a 2-digit positive integer such that the number '1' formed by the first digit is divisible by 1 and the number '12' formed by the first two digits is divisible by 2.

(a) How many 3-digit positive integers '*abc*' are there, where *a*, *b*, *c* are the digits 1, 2, 3 in some order, such that '*a*' is divisible by 1, '*ab*' is divisible by 2 and '*abc*' is divisible by 3?

(b) How many 4-digit positive integers '*abcd*' are there, where *a*, *b*, *c*, *d* are the digits 1, 2, 3, 4 in some order, such that '*a*' is divisible by 1, '*ab*' is divisible by 2, '*abc*' is divisible by 3 and '*abcd*' is divisible by 4?

(c) How many 5-digit positive integers '*abcde*' are there, where *a*, *b*, *c*, *d*, *e* are the digits 1, 2, 3, 4, 5 in some order, such that '*a*' is divisible by 1, '*ab*' is divisible by 2, '*abc*' is divisible by 3, '*abcd*' is divisible by 4 and '*abcde*' is divisible by 5?

(d) How many 6-digit positive integers '*abcdef*' are there, where *a*, *b*, *c*, *d*, *e*, *f* are the digits 1, 2, 3, 4, 5, 6 in some order, such that '*a*' is divisible by 1, '*ab*' is divisible by 2, '*abc*' is divisible by 3, '*abcd*' is divisible by 4, '*abcde*' is divisible by 5 and '*abcdef*' is divisible by 6?

B6 **6.** The sum of four different prime numbers is a prime number. The sum of some pair of the numbers is a prime number, as is the sum of some triple of the numbers.

What is the smallest possible sum of the four prime numbers?

Chapter 10

More algebra

Example

Mr Gallop has two stables which each initially housed three ponies. His prize pony, Rein Beau, is worth £250 000. Usually Rein Beau spends his day in the small stable, but when he wandered across into the large stable, Mr Gallop was surprised to find that the average value of the ponies in each stable rose by £10 000.

What is the total value of all six ponies?

Discussion

At the start, it looks as if there are six unknowns, one for each of the ponies. This problem can be solved by introducing six letters, but it is more efficient to think about how the ponies are grouped.

It is important to define any letter that you introduce clearly rather than just write down an equation.

Also, to avoid unwieldy arithmetic, defining the letters in terms of thousands of pounds removes extra zeros.

Solution

Let the total value of the two unnamed ponies in the small stable be v thousand pounds, and let the total value of the three unnamed ponies in the large stable be s thousand pounds.

Working in thousands of pounds, for the small stable, the initial average value was $\dfrac{v + 250}{3}$ and the final average was $\dfrac{v}{2}$. Therefore

$$\frac{v}{2} = \frac{v + 250}{3} + 10.$$

Multiplying each term by 6, we get

$$3v = 2v + 500 + 60,$$

so that, subtracting $2v$ from each side, we have

$$v = 560.$$

For the large stable, the initial average was $\dfrac{s}{3}$ and the final average $\dfrac{s + 250}{4}$. Therefore

$$\frac{s + 250}{4} = \frac{s}{3} + 10.$$

Multiplying each term by 12, we obtain

$$3s + 750 = 4s + 120,$$

so that, subtracting $3s$ and 120 from each side, we have

$$s = 630.$$

Thus $v + s + 250 = 560 + 630 + 250$, which equals 1440, so the total value of all six ponies is £1 440 000.

CHECK

$$\frac{560\,000 + 250\,000}{3} = 270\,000,$$

which is 10 000 more than

$$\frac{560\,000}{2} = 280\,000.$$

Also

$$\frac{630\,000}{3} = 210\,000,$$

which is 10 000 less than

$$\frac{630\,000 + 250\,000}{4} = 220\,000.$$

Exercise 10

B2 **1.** Pippa thinks of a number. She adds 1 to it to get a second number. She then adds 2 to the second number to get a third number, adds 3 to the third to get a fourth, and finally adds 4 to the fourth to get a fifth number.

Pippa's brother Ben also thinks of a number but he subtracts 1 to get a second. He then subtracts 2 from the second to get a third, and so on until he too has five numbers.

They discover that the sum of Pippa's five numbers is the same as the sum of Ben's five numbers. What is the difference between the two numbers of which they first thought?

B3 **2.** Jack and Jill went up a hill. They started at the same time, but Jack arrived at the top one-and-a-half hours before Jill. On the way down, Jill calculated that, if she had walked 50% faster and Jack had walked 50% slower, then they would have arrived at the top of the hill at the same time.

How long did Jill actually take to walk up to the top of the hill?

B3 **3.** When Dad gave out the pocket money, Amy received twice as much as her first brother, three times as much as the second, four times as much as the third and five times as much as the last brother. Peter complained that he had received 30p less than Tom.

Use this information to find all the possible amounts of money that Amy could have received.

B5 **4.** Calum and his friend cycle from A to C, passing through B.

During the trip he asks his friend how far they have cycled.

His friend replies "one third as far as it is from here to B".

Ten miles later Calum asks him how far they have to cycle to reach C.

His friend replies again "one third as far as it is from here to B".

How far from A will Calum have cycled when he reaches C?

B6 **5.** The diagram is to be completed so that each white square contains a different whole number from 1 to 12 inclusive, and also so that the four numbers in the set of squares along each edge have the same total.

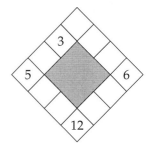

In how many different ways can the diagram be completed correctly?

B6 **6.** The numbers 1 to 7 are to be placed in the seven regions formed by three overlapping circles, with 6 in the central region, so that there is one number inside each region and the total of the numbers inside each circle is T.

What values of T are possible?

B6 **7.** In a sequence of positive integers, each term is larger than the previous term. Also, after the first two terms, each term is the sum of the previous two terms.

The eighth term of the sequence is 390. What is the ninth term?

B6 **8.** Sam has put sweets in five jars in such a way that no jar is empty and no two jars contain the same number of sweets. Also, any three jars contain more sweets in total than the total of the remaining two jars.

What is the smallest possible number of sweets altogether in the five jars?

B6 **9.** Pat has a number of counters to place into the cells of a 3×3 grid like the one shown. She may place any number of counters in each cell or leave some of the cells empty. She then finds the number of counters in each row and each column. Pat is trying to place counters in such a way that these six totals are all different.

What is the smallest total number of counters that Pat can use?

B6 **10.** The letters a, b, c, d, e, f represent single digits and each letter represents a different digit. They satisfy the following equations:

$$a + b = d, \quad b + c = e \quad \text{and} \quad d + e = f.$$

Find all possible solutions for the values of a, b, c, d, e and f.

Chapter 11

Miscellany

Example

Catherine has 200 coins. She gives a number of children some coins so that

(i) every child has at least one coin;

(ii) no two children have the same number of coins.

What is the largest number of children who might receive coins?

Discussion

In this example, it might seem difficult to find a starting point. A good strategy is to think of a simpler problem and build up an idea from that.

When there are two children, the smallest number of coins that Catherine can give is 3 since $1 + 2 = 3$.

Let us consider the smallest number of coins she would give to three children. Because $1 + 2 + 3 = 6$, Catherine would need at least 6 coins for three children.

Continuing in this way, we see that Catherine could give a minimum of $1 + 2 + 3 + 4 = 10$ coins to 4 children.

Looking at small examples like this gives us an idea of what is happening, so let us move on to the actual question.

Solution

Recall that *the sum of the integers from 1 to n is equal to* $\frac{1}{2}n(n+1)$.

Suppose that Catherine gives 1 coin to the first child, 2 coins to the next, and so on. If there are 20 children, she will have given

$$\frac{1}{2} \times 20(20 + 1) = 10 \times 21$$
$$= 210,$$

and so Catherine cannot give 200 coins to 20 children (or more), assuming that no two receive the same number of coins.

Can we show that Catherine may give 200 coins to 19 children?

Well, we know that the sum of the integers from 1 to 19 is equal to

$$\frac{1}{2} \times 19(19 + 1) = 19 \times 10$$
$$= 190,$$

in other words

$$1 + 2 + 3 + 4 + 5 + 6 + 7 + 8 + 9 + 10 + 11 + 12 + 13 + 14$$
$$+ 15 + 16 + 17 + 18 + 19 = 190.$$

This gives a way of distributing 190 coins to 19 children. Is it possible to add another 10 coins to this distribution, whilst keeping the condition that no two children have the same number of coins?

There are, of course, many ways to do this. One way is to arrange for Catherine to give another 10 coins to one particular child so that the number that child receives is still different from any others. For example, she could give 25 coins instead of 15 to one child, so that she distributes the 200 coins to 19 children in the following way:

$$1 + 2 + 3 + 4 + 5 + 6 + 7 + 8 + 9 + 10 + 11 + 12 + 13 + 14$$
$$+ 25 + 16 + 17 + 18 + 19 = 200,$$

Hence it is possible for Catherine to give the coins to 19 children.

However, we showed above that Catherine cannot give 200 coins to more than 19 children. Therefore the largest number of children who could receive coins is 19.

Example

A large marzipan cube is made up of 27 small cubes, as shown. A bug eats the small cubes one by one; each time the bug finishes eating one, it passes to a neighbouring small cube (that shared a face with the one just eaten) and starts eating that.

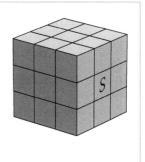

The bug wants to start by eating the cube marked S in the diagram, and wants to end by eating the central cube.

Prove that this is impossible.

Discussion

This type of problem, along with many problems about chessboards, can be solved using a *colouring argument*.

Solution

Colour the small cubes "alternately", so that no two cubes of the same colour are neighbours (that is, share a face). Suppose we use green and yellow, with green for the corner cubes.

The cube S is then green, so the bug wants to start on a green cube. But the bug eats small cubes of alternate colours and there are 27 small cubes in all. So the bug will finish with a green cube.

However, the central small cube is yellow, so the bug cannot finish there.

Exercise 11

B1 **1.** Tamsin has a selection of cubical boxes whose internal dimensions are whole numbers of centimetres, that is, $1\,\text{cm} \times 1\,\text{cm} \times 1\,\text{cm}$, $2\,\text{cm} \times 2\,\text{cm} \times 2\,\text{cm}$, and so on.

What are the dimensions of the smallest of these boxes in which Tamsin could fit ten rectangular blocks each measuring $3\,\text{cm} \times 2\,\text{cm} \times 1\,\text{cm}$ without the blocks extending outside the box?

B2 **2.** Five teams played in a competition and every team played once against each of the other four teams. Each team received three points for a match it won, one point for a match it drew and no points for a match it lost. At the end of the competition the points were:

> Yellows 10, Reds 9, Greens 4, Blues 3 and Pinks 1.

(a) How many of the matches resulted in a draw?

(b) What were the results of Greens' matches against the other four teams?

B2 **3.** Five children, boys Vince, Will, and Zac and girls Xenia and Yvonne, sit at a round table. They come from five different cities, Aberdeen, Belfast, Cardiff, Durham and Edinburgh. The child from Aberdeen sits between Zac and the child from Edinburgh. Neither of the two girls is sitting next to Will. Vince sits between Yvonne and the child from Durham. Zac writes to the child from Cardiff.

Find, giving reasons, where each child comes from.

B2 **4.** An example of a particular type of number chain is shown below.

$$97 \rightarrow 63 \rightarrow 18 \rightarrow 8$$

The first number is a positive integer. Each number after the first is the product of the digits of the previous number, so in this case $63 = 9 \times 7$; $18 = 6 \times 3$; $8 = 1 \times 8$. The chain stops when a single-digit number is reached.

Suppose that in such a chain the final number is 6. Find all possible two-digit first numbers for this chain.

B3 **5.** Alice, the March Hare and the Mock Turtle were the only three competitors at the Wonderland sports day, and all three of them competed in each event. The scoring system was exactly the same for each event: the points awarded for first, second and third places were all positive integers and (even in Wonderland) more points were awarded for first place than for second, and more points for second place than third.

Of course, the March Hare won the Sack Race. At the end of the day, Alice had scored 18 points while the Mock Turtle had 9 points and the March Hare 8 points.

Can you decide how many events there were?

And can you tell who came last in the 'Egg and Spoon' race?

B4 **6.** (a) Network A has nine edges which meet at six nodes. The numbers 1, 2, 3, 4, 5, 6 are placed at the nodes, with a different number at each node.

Is it possible to do this so that the sum of the two numbers at the ends of an edge is different for each edge? Either show a way of doing this, or prove that it is impossible.

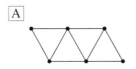

(b) Repeat the same procedure for network B, that is, show that it is possible to place the six numbers so that the sum of the two numbers at the ends of an edge is different for each edge, or prove that it is impossible to do so.

B4 **7.** For each positive two-digit integer, Jack subtracts the units digit from the tens digit; for example, the number 34 gives $3 - 4 = -1$.

What is the sum of all his results?

B4 **8.** There are 20 sweets on the table. Two players take turns to eat as many sweets as they choose, but they must eat at least one, and never more than half of what remains. The loser is the player who has no valid move.

Is it possible for one of the two players to force the other to lose? If so, how?

Chapter 12

More geometry

Example

The diagram shows part of a ring of squares and triangles around a regular polygon which has vertices $A, B, C, D, E, \ldots$.

(a) Suppose the polygon $ABCDE\ldots$ has 10 sides. Calculate the sizes of $\angle ABC$ and $\angle PQB$.

(b) Suppose the regular polygon has N sides.
Find the value of the ratio of the size of $\angle ABC$ to the size of $\angle PQB$.

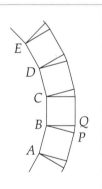

Discussion

At first glance, this is a problem about polygons. So a solution is likely to include calculating the size of the interior angle in a regular polygon (we have several ways of doing this).

However, a closer look shows that triangles may also be involved; triangles certainly appear in the diagram. Also, the word regular suggests we should look for a triangle which has equal sides, in other words, we look for an isosceles triangle. Then we can use the facts we know about isosceles triangles.

Solution

(a) Using *the size of each exterior angle of a regular polygon with n sides is equal to* $360° \div n$, we find that the exterior angle of a regular polygon with ten sides is $360° \div 10 = 36°$. Since $\angle ABC$ is an interior angle of the polygon, from *the sum of the angles on a straight line is 180°*, we obtain $\angle ABC = 180° - 36°$, which is $144°$. Also, each of angles PBA and CBQ is equal to $90°$ because they are angles at the vertex of a square.

Using the result *the sum of the angles round a point is 360°* for point B, we get

$$\angle ABC + \angle PBA + \angle PBQ + \angle CBQ = 360°$$

so that

$$144° + 90° + \angle QBP + 90° = 360°$$

and hence

$$\angle QBP + 324° = 360°.$$

Therefore, subtracting $324°$ from each side, we obtain

$$\angle QBP = 36°.$$

Now $PB = BA$ because they are sides of a square. Similarly $CB = BQ$. But the polygon is regular, so all its sides have equal length. Therefore $AB = BC$, and hence $PB = BQ$.

Thus triangle QBP is isosceles, and from *the angles opposite equal sides of a triangle are equal*, it follows that $\angle BPQ = \angle PQB$.

Using *the sum of the angles in a triangle is 180°* for triangle QBP, we obtain

$$\angle PQB + \angle BPQ + \angle QBP = 180°$$

so that

$$2 \times \angle PQB + 36° = 180°.$$

Subtracting $36°$ from each side, we get

$$2 \times \angle PQB = 180° - 36°$$
$$= 144°.$$

Finally, dividing each side by 2, we obtain

$$\angle PQB = 72°.$$

Fac
17.5
p 11

Fac
17.2
p 10

Fac
17.2
p 10

Fa·
17.4
p 1·

Fa·
17.·
p 1·

(b) We may use exactly the same method as in part (a) to find the values of $\angle ABC$ and $\angle PQB$, but this time in terms of N.

An alternative method is as follows.

Firstly, as shown in part (a), triangle QBP is isosceles and therefore, using *the angles opposite equal sides of a triangle are equal*, it follows that $\angle BPQ = \angle PQB$.

Now consider triangle QBP. Extend PB to X, as in the following figure, so that $\angle XBQ$ is an exterior angle of triangle QBP.

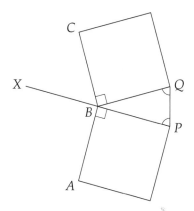

Using *the exterior angle of a triangle is equal to the sum of the two interior opposite angles* for triangle QBP, we get

$$\angle XBQ = \angle BPQ + \angle PQB$$
$$= 2 \times \angle PQB.$$

But $\angle CBQ = 90°$ because it is an angle of a square. Similarly $\angle PBA = 90°$, so that, using *the sum of the angles on a straight line is 180°*, we obtain $\angle ABX = 90°$.

It follows that $\angle ABC$ and $\angle XBQ$ are equal, since they are each equal to $\angle XBC + 90°$.

Hence $\angle ABC = 2 \times \angle PQB$ and therefore $\angle ABC : \angle PQB = 2 : 1$.

REMARK Notice that the answer is does not involve the value of N.

Exercise 12

B1 **1.** In the rectangle $ABCD$, M and N are the midpoints of AB and CD respectively; AB has length 2 and AD has length 1.

Given that $\angle ABD = x°$, calculate $\angle DZN$ in terms of x.

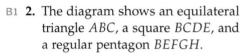

B1 **2.** The diagram shows an equilateral triangle ABC, a square $BCDE$, and a regular pentagon $BEFGH$.

Which angle is larger: $\angle ADE$ or $\angle AHE$?

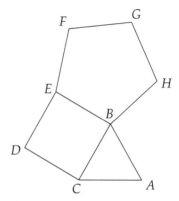

B2 **3.** The diagram shows a quadrilateral $ABCD$ in which AB, BC and AD are all of length 1 unit, $\angle BAD$ is a right angle and $\angle ABC$ is 60°.

Prove that $\angle CDB = 2 \times \angle DBC$.

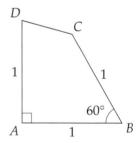

B3 **4.** Two squares $BAXY$ and $CBZT$ are drawn on the outside of a regular hexagon $ABCDEF$, and two squares $CDPQ$ and $DERS$ are drawn on the inside, as shown.

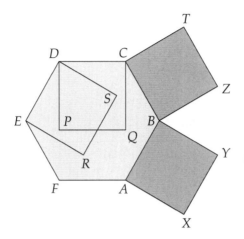

Prove that $PS = YZ$.

B4 **5.** A regular polygon P with n sides is divided into two pieces by a single straight cut.
One piece is a triangle T, the other is a polygon Q with m sides.

How are m and n related?

B4 **6.** The point F lies inside the regular pentagon $ABCDE$ so that $ABFE$ is a rhombus.

Prove that EFC is a straight line.

B5 **7.** $ABCDE$ is a pentagon in which triangles ABC, AED and CAD are all isosceles, $AC = AD$, $\angle CAD$ is acute. Interior angles ABC and AED are both right angles.

Draw a sketch of pentagon $ABCDE$, marking all the equal sides and equal angles.

Show how to fit four such identical pentagons together to form a hexagon. Explain how you know the pentagons will fit exactly.

B5 **8.** The diagram shows part of a regular 20-sided polygon (an icosagon) $ABCDEF\ldots$, a square $BCYZ$ and a regular pentagon $DEVWX$.

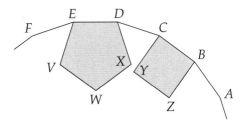

Show that the vertex X lies on the line DY.

B5 **9.** Three identical, non-overlapping squares $ABCD$, $AEFG$, $AHIJ$ (all labelled anticlockwise) are joined at the point A so that:

   (i) they appear anticlockwise in the order given; and

   (ii) they are 'equally spread' (so that $\angle JAB = \angle DAE = \angle GAH$).

Calculate $\angle GBH$.

Chapter 13

Another miscellany

Example

An ant wishes to make a circuit of the board shown, visiting each square exactly once and returning to the starting square. At each step the ant moves to an adjacent square across an edge. Two circuits are considered to be the same if the first follows the same path as the second but either starts at a different square or follows the same path in reverse.

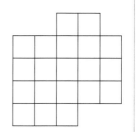

How many such circuits are possible?

Discussion

Many questions of this type may be completely unfamiliar and you may not have any idea how to begin. That should not put you off. The best way to proceed is to read the question carefully before you start to write. Then, do not be afraid to discard your first attempt and attempt another completely different one. This is normal for problems of a type we have never seen before.

There is usually no single strategy to answer these questions—no single way to plan a route to a solution. The best tactic is to read the question several times and look for something which is essential and individual to that question.

In this particular example, the crucial observation is that there is a limited number of ways to exit a square once it has been entered. (The solution we give uses the fact that there are essentially only two types of path across a square.)

Finally, if you think that there is only one route through a particular square, then your solution should make it clear why that is true.

Solution

Notice that, in order to form a circuit of the required form, there are exactly two ways that the ant can travel through a square:

corner
the ant enters through an edge and leaves from the adjacent edge, that is the path forms a right angle around the corner of a square;

straight
the ant enters through one edge and leaves from the opposite parallel edge, that is, travels straight across the square.

We therefore consider building up the path of the ant by adding two kinds of tile to the board, a corner tile and a straight tile, as shown in the following figures.

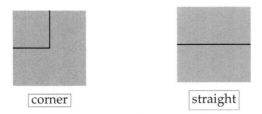

Of course, each tile may be rotated before it is placed on the board.

There is no choice in the seven corners, so we may immediately add seven corner tiles (see figure 1). There is now no choice for the marked squares in figure 1, so we add a corner tile and two straight tiles (see figure 2).

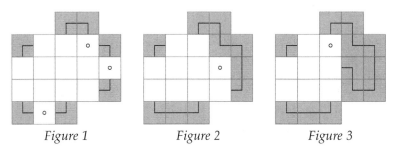

Figure 1   Figure 2   Figure 3

Consider the marked square in figure 2. Two edges have already been used, so we have to get in and out across the other two edges. We therefore add another corner tile here. After doing this, there is no choice for the square below, so we add yet another corner tile (see figure 3).

Now consider the marked square in figure 3. Adding a straight tile here would force us to place a corner tile in the square below. However, this would form a closed loop on the right-hand side of the board, so that we would not have made a circuit of the whole board. Therefore we can only place a corner tile in the marked square, which forces us to place a straight tile to its left (see figure 4).

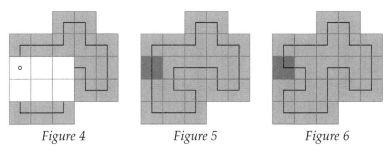

Figure 4   Figure 5   Figure 6

Finally, consider the marked square in figure 4. We may place either a straight tile or a corner tile in this square. In either case, the remaining tiles are forced: the straight tile gives the circuit shown in figure 5; and the corner tile gives the circuit shown in figure 6.

Therefore exactly two circuits of the required form are possible.

Exercise 13

B5 **1.** On an adventure holiday five children, called *A, B, C, D, E,* all take part in five competitions, called *V, W, X, Y, Z.* In each competition marks of 5, 4, 3, 2, 1 are awarded for coming 1st, 2nd, 3rd, 4th or 5th respectively. There are no ties for places.

Child *A* scores a total of 24 marks, child *C* scores the same in each of four competitions, child *D* scores 4 in competition *V,* and child *E* scores 5 in *W* and 3 in *X.* Surprisingly, their overall positions are in alphabetical order.

Show that this information is enough to find all the scores, and that there is only one solution. Give the marks scored by each child in each competition by filling in a copy of this table.

	V	W	X	Y	Z	Total
A						
B						
C						
D						
E						

B5 **2.** An intelligent bug starts at the point $(4,0)$ and follows these instructions:

(i) first face "East" and walk one unit to the point $(5,0)$;

(ii) from then on, whenever you arrive at a point (x,y) with x and y both integers,

either turn left through $90°$ if $x - y$ is a multiple of 4 or is 1 more than a multiple of 4;

or turn right through $90°$ if $x - y$ is 2 more than a multiple of 4 or is 3 more than a multiple of 4;

and then walk one unit to the next point whose coordinates are both integers.

After one move, the bug is at the point $(5,0)$.

(a) Where will the bug be after 12 moves?

(b) Where will the bug be after 50 moves?

B6 **3.** Two players X and Y play a game on a board which consists of a narrow strip that is one square wide and n squares long. They take turns placing counters, which are one square wide and two squares long, on unoccupied squares on the board.

A counter.

The first player who cannot go loses. X always plays first, and both players always make the best available move.

(a) Who wins the game on a 4×1 board? Explain how they must play to win and why they are certain to win.

(b) Who wins the game on a 5×1 board? Explain why. So who wins on a 7×1 board?

(c) Who wins on a 6×1 board? How?

(d) Who wins on an 8×1 board? How?

B6 **4.** X and Y play a game in which X starts by choosing a number, which must be either 1 or 2.

Y then adds either 1 or 2 and states the total of the two numbers chosen so far. X does likewise, adding either 1 or 2 and stating the total, and so on. The winner is the first person to make the total reach (or exceed) 20.

(a) Explain how X can always win.

(b) The game is now modified so that at each stage the number chosen must be either 1 or 2 or 4. Which of X and Y can now always win and how?

B6 **5.** This question is about ways of placing square tiles on a square grid, all the squares being the same size. Each tile is divided by a diagonal into two regions, one grey and one white. Such a tile can be placed on the grid in one of four different positions, as shown.

When two tiles meet along an edge (side by side or one below the other) the two regions which touch must be of different types (that is, one grey and one white).

(a) A 2×2 grid of four squares is to be covered by four tiles.

(i) If the top-left square is covered by a tile in position A, find all the possible ways in which the other three squares may be covered.

(ii) In how many different ways can a 2×2 grid be covered by four tiles?

(b) In how many different ways can a 3×3 grid be covered by nine tiles?

(c) Explaining your reasoning, find a formula for the number of different ways in which a square grid measuring $n \times n$ can be covered by n^2 tiles.

B6 **6.** A game for two players uses four counters on a board which consists of a 20 × 1 rectangle. The two players take it in turns to move one counter. A turn consists of moving any one of the four counters any number of squares to the right, but the counter may not land on top of, or move past, any of the other counters. For instance, in the position shown, the next player could move *D* one, two or three squares to the right, or move *C* one or two squares to the right, and so on.

The winner of the game is the player who makes the last legal move. (After this move the counters will occupy the four squares on the extreme right of the board and no further legal moves will be possible.)

In the position shown above, it is your turn. Which move should you make and what should be your strategy in subsequent moves to ensure that you will win the game?

B6 **7.** We want to colour red some of the cells in the 4 × 4 grid shown so that wherever the L-shaped piece is placed on the grid it covers at least one red cell. The L-shaped piece may only cover complete cells, may be rotated, but may not be turned over and may not extend beyond the grid.

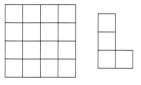

(a) Show that it is possible to achieve this by colouring exactly four cells red.

(b) Show that it is impossible to achieve this by colouring fewer than four cells red.

B6 **8.** I want to choose a list of *n* different numbers from the first 20 positive integers so that no two of my numbers differ by 5.

What is the largest value of *n* for which this is possible?

How many different lists are there with this many numbers?

B6 **9.** The integer 23 173 is such that

    (i) every pair of neighbouring digits, taken in order, forms a prime number; and

    (ii) all of these prime numbers are different.

What is the largest integer which meets these conditions?

B6 **10.** On the 5 × 4 grid shown, I am only allowed to move from one square to a neighbouring square by crossing an edge. So the squares I visit alternate between grey and white. I have to start on a grey square and visit each grey square exactly once.

What is the smallest number of white squares that I have to visit?

Prove that your answer is indeed the smallest.

(If I visit a white square more than once, I only count it as one white square visited.)

Chapter 14

Constructions

Some problems can be solved by adding one or more lines (usually straight lines) to a figure. In some cases this leads to a dissection.

Example

The regular hexagon *ABCDEF* has sides of length 2. The point *P* is the midpoint of *AB*, *Q* is the midpoint of *BC*, and so on.

Find the area of the hexagon *PQRSTU*.

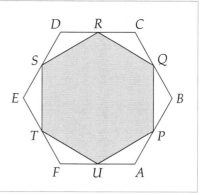

Discussion

This question relies on an understanding of equilateral triangles and the right-angled triangle found when one of its medians is drawn.

There are many ways of solving this problem. We present a method that uses two dissections, but does not use sophisticated techniques.

Solution

We may divide the original hexagon into 24 triangles, as shown in the following figure.

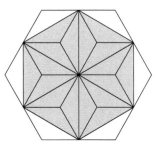

We need to confirm that all these triangles are "the same" and that they fit together as indicated. This is possible because each triangle has angles of $120°$, $30°$ and $30°$, and the sides all match—each triangle shares an edge with at least one neighbour.

Now the shaded hexagon $PQRSTU$ is composed of 18 of these 24 triangles, so the area of $PQRSTU$ is three-quarters of the area of the hexagon $ABCDEF$ (because $18 \div 24 = 3 \div 4$).

So if we can find the area of the hexagon $ABCDEF$, then we can find the required area. How can we find the area of $ABCDEF$? Well, we use the fact that *a regular hexagon may be dissected into six equilateral triangles* to divide the hexagon $ABCDEF$, as shown in the following figure.

Fa
17.
p 1

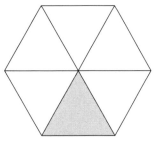

Each of the equilateral triangles has sides of length 2. In order to find the area of one of them, we first use *an equilateral triangle with sides of length 2 has height $\sqrt{3}$*. Thus the height of the triangle is equal to $\sqrt{3}$. Now using *the area of a triangle is equal to $\frac{1}{2} \times base \times height$*, we find that the area of one equilateral triangle is

Fa
18.
p
Fa
18.
p

$$\tfrac{1}{2} \times 2 \times \sqrt{3} = \sqrt{3}.$$

Hence the area of the hexagon $ABCDEF$ is $6 \times \sqrt{3}$. But the area of the hexagon $PQRSTU$ is three-quarters of this, which is

$$\frac{3}{4} \times 6 \times \sqrt{3} = \frac{18}{4} \times \sqrt{3}$$
$$= \frac{9}{2} \times \sqrt{3}$$
$$= \frac{9\sqrt{3}}{2}.$$

Exercise 14

B3 **1.** In the diagram, O is the centre of the circle. The lengths of AB and BC are both 10 cm. The area of quadrilateral $OABC$ is 120 cm^2.

Calculate the radius of the circle.

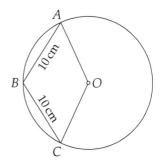

B3 **2.** A point lying somewhere inside a parallelogram is joined to the four vertices, thus creating four triangles T, U, V and W, as shown.

Prove that

area T + area V = area U + area W.

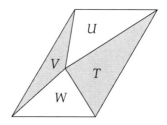

B4 **3.** In the square $ABCD$, S is the point one quarter of the way from A to B, and T is the point one quarter of the way from B to A. The points U, V, W, X, Y, Z are defined similarly. The eight points S, T, U, V, W, X, Y, Z lie on a circle, whose centre is at the centre of the square.

Determine which has the larger area: the square $ABCD$, or the circle.

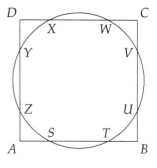

B4 **4.** Start with an equilateral triangle ABC of side 2 units, and construct three outward-pointing squares $ABPQ$, $BCTU$, $CARS$ on the three sides AB, BC, CA.

What is the area of the hexagon $PQRSTU$?

B4 **5.** In the polygon *ABCDEFG* shown in the diagram, *FG* = 6 and *GA* = *AB* = *BC* = *CD* = *DE* = *EF*. Also, *BDFG* is a square.

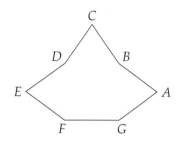

The area of the whole polygon is exactly twice the area of *BDFG*.

Find the length of the perimeter of the polygon.

B5 **6.** The diagram shows two squares *ACEG* and *PQRS* inside a regular octagon *ABCDEFGH* which has sides of length 2 cm.

What fraction of the entire octagon is shaded?

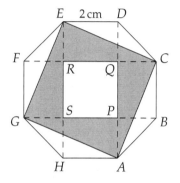

B5 **7.** A window is constructed of six identical panes of glass. Each pane is a pentagon with two adjacent sides of length two units. The other three sides of each pentagon, which are on the perimeter of the window, form half of the boundary of a regular hexagon.

Calculate the exact area of glass in the window.

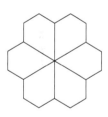

B5 **8.** In the diagram, the rectangle *ABCD* is divided into three congruent rectangles. The line segment *JK* divides *CDFG* into two parts of equal area.

What is the area of triangle *AEI* as a fraction of the area of *ABCD*?

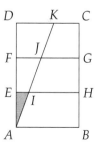

B6 **9.** Points A, B, C, D, E and F are equally spaced around a circle of radius 1. The circle is divided into six sectors as shown in figure 1.

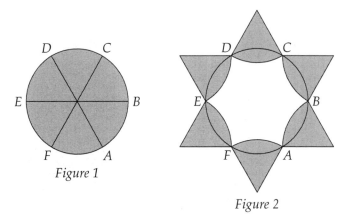

Figure 1

Figure 2

The six sectors are then rearranged so that A, B, C, D, E and F lie on a new circle, also of radius 1, as shown in figure 2, with the sectors pointing outwards.

Find the area of the curvy *unshaded* region.

Part II

Reference

Chapter 15

Arithmetic

Arithmetic is the branch of mathematics which deals with relationships between numbers, and which uses basic operations such as addition, subtraction, multiplication and division to deal with problems involving numbers.

Some commonly used terms are defined in the glossary on page 255.

15.1 Numbers

Examples of numbers are 4, $\frac{2}{7}$, 2.6, -8, $\sqrt{5}$ and π.

Types of number

The *natural numbers* are the counting numbers 1, 2, 3, ...

The *integers* consist of the negatives of all the natural numbers, zero, and all the natural numbers, that is, ..., -4, -3, -2, -1, 0, 1, 2, 3, ...

Some of the problems in this book involve working with integers only. This can make a big difference when you are trying to solve a problem, because it (usually) reduces the number of possible solutions to something manageable.

For example, suppose you want to solve the equation $ab = 6$. In general, there is an infinite number of possible values for a and b— such as $a = \frac{4}{5}$, $b = \frac{15}{2}$—and you cannot find either a or b without first knowing the other. But if you are told that a and b are integers, then there only four possibilities, such as $a = -1$, $b = -6$. (Can you find the other three possibilities?)

Consecutive integers follow one another, without gaps, in the list of all integers. For example, 34 and 35 are consecutive numbers, as are 23, 24, 25, 26, 27 and 28, as well as -2, -1, 0, 1, 2, 3. A list of consecutive integers alternates between even and odd numbers (or *vice versa*), so it follows either the pattern 'even, odd, even, odd, ...' or the pattern 'odd, even, odd, even, ...'.

Zero

Because $0 \times n = 0$ and $n \times 0 = 0$, zero is a multiple of any integer n. However, it is important to remember that *division by zero* is not allowed.

Note that zero is *even* since it is a multiple of 2.

Digits

In the common numerical system, 0, 1, 2, 3, 4, 5, 6, 7, 8 and 9 are used to represent any number. These ten numbers are called *digits*. For example, the integer 705 is a three-digit integer.

By convention, 0 cannot be the first (that is, leftmost) digit.

Powers

Powers, sometimes called *indices*, are a shorthand way of writing products of the same number. Thus $2 \times 2 \times 2 \times 2 \times 2 \times 2$ can be written as 2^6, $5 \times 5 \times 5 \times 3 \times 3$ can be written as $5^3 \times 3^2$, and 1.1^4 means $1.1 \times 1.1 \times 1.1 \times 1.1$.

15.2 Sequences of integers

Some well-known sequences of integers can be represented by placing dots in a pattern. Figure 15.1 shows the first few *squares* and figure 15.2 shows the first few *triangular numbers*.

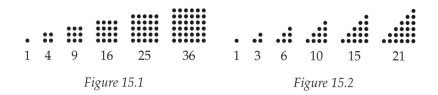

| 1 | 4 | 9 | 16 | 25 | 36 | | 1 | 3 | 6 | 10 | 15 | 21 |

Figure 15.1   *Figure 15.2*

Squares

The sequence of squares is 1, 4, 9, 16, 25, 36, 49, 64, 81, 100, 121, 144, 169, 196, ... It is well worth becoming familiar with these.

Consider the nth square, which contains n^2 dots. Divide the square into L-shapes, in the manner shown in figure 15.3.

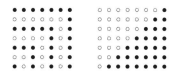

Figure 15.3   *Figure 15.4*

There is 1 dot in the first 'L-shape', and each L-shape after the first may be obtained from the next smaller one by adding one more dot at each end. Therefore the number of dots in each L-shape is 2 more than the next smaller one, so there are

$$1, 3, 5, 7, 9, \ldots,$$

dots in the L-shapes—each term is the next odd number. The number of L-shapes altogether is n, so that

Fact 15.2A
The sum of the first n odd positive integers is equal to n^2.

Triangular numbers

Now consider the nth triangular number. Combine two triangles to form a rectangle, in the manner shown in figure 15.4. The rectangle has dimensions n and $n + 1$, so the number of dots in the rectangle is $n \times (n + 1)$ and each triangle has half this number of dots. It follows that

Fact 15.2B
The nth triangular number is equal to $\frac{1}{2}n(n + 1)$.

The sequence of triangular numbers is 1, 3, 6, 10, 15, 21, 28, 35, 44, ...

By considering each pattern of dots in figure 15.2 row by row, we may write the sequence of triangular numbers in the form

$$1,$$
$$1 + 2,$$
$$1 + 2 + 3,$$
$$1 + 2 + 3 + 4,$$
$$\ldots,$$

in which each term is a sum of natural numbers. In other words, the nth triangular number is equal to the sum of the integers from 1 to n, that is, $1 + 2 + 3 + \cdots + n$. Using fact 15.2B, it follows that

Fact 15.2C

The sum of the integers from 1 to n is equal to $\frac{1}{2}n(n + 1)$.

Fibonacci numbers

A sequence of integers that you may come across is 1, 1, 2, 3, 5, 8, 13, 21, ..., which begins 1, 1, and every following term is the sum of the previous two terms. These integers are the *Fibonacci numbers*.

A sequence like 11, 14, 25, 39, 64, ... may also be considered to be a *Fibonacci sequence*—even though it does not begin 1, 1—because each term after the first two is the sum of the previous two terms.

Cubes

The sequence of *cubes* is 1, 8, 27, 64, 125, 216, 343, ... It is well worth becoming familiar with these.

15.3   Factors, divisibility and primes

Factors

We say that the positive integer n is a *factor* of the integer m whenever m is an integer multiple of n, that is, $m = k \times n$ for some integer k.

So 14, say, is a factor of an integer m if $m = 14k$ for some integer k. For example, 14 is a factor of 154 since $154 = 11 \times 14$.

Divisibility

Another way of saying that *n* is a factor of *m* is to say that *m* is *divisible* by *n*. So an integer is divisible by two when it has the form 2*k* for some integer *k*; similarly, an integer is divisible by three when it has the form 3*k* for some integer *k*; and so on.

In the following, the term 'last' is used to mean 'rightmost'. So the last digit of an integer is the same as the units digit.

Fact 15.3A

An integer is divisible by 2 when the last digit is even, and not otherwise.

This follows from the fact that 10 is divisible by 2, and so to test divisibility it is only necessary to consider the units digit.

Fact 15.3B

An integer is divisible by 3 when the sum of the digits is divisible by 3, and not otherwise.

Fact 15.3C

An integer is divisible by 4 when the integer formed by the last two digits is divisible by 4, and not otherwise.

This follows from the fact that 100 is divisible by 4.

Fact 15.3D

An integer is divisible by 5 when the last digit is 0 or 5, and not otherwise.

This follows from the fact that 10 is divisible by 5.

Fact 15.3E

An integer is divisible by 8 when the integer formed by the last three digits is divisible by 8, and not otherwise.

This follows from the fact that 1000 is divisible by 8.

Fact 15.3F

An integer is divisible by 9 when the sum of the digits is divisible by 9, and not otherwise.

Primes

An integer is *prime* when it is greater than 1 and it has no divisors other than 1 and itself; otherwise it is not prime.

The first few prime numbers are 2, 3, 5, 7, 11, 13, ... Note that there is only one even prime number, namely 2. Also note that the number 1 is not a prime number.

Considering the factors of a prime number, we observe:

Fact 15.3G

A prime number has exactly two *factors, namely 1 and itself.*

To see whether or not an integer is prime, it is only necessary to look for prime factors no bigger than its square root. This is because, as long as the integer is neither a square nor a prime, its divisors occur in pairs, one smaller than the square root and the other larger than it. You should look at a few examples to see how this works.

> For example, to see whether 167 is prime, since $13^2 = 169$ is greater than 167, try dividing 167 in turn by 2, 3, 5, 7 and 11. None of these is a factor of 167, so we conclude that 167 is prime.

Fact 15.3H (The fundamental theorem of arithmetic)

Every integer greater than 1 is either a prime number or the product of prime numbers.

> For example,
>
> $$280 = 2 \times 2 \times 2 \times 5 \times 7$$
> $$= 2^3 \times 5 \times 7,$$
> $$111 = 3 \times 37$$
> $$\text{and} \quad 1001 = 7 \times 11 \times 13.$$

In all cases, there is exactly one way to write a number as a product of prime factors (ignoring the order).

Fact 15.3I

The prime factors of a square occur in pairs.

Thus $296 = (2 \times 2) \times (7 \times 7) \times (7 \times 7)$ is a square and $295 = 5 \times (7 \times 7)$ is not.

Fact 15.3J

The prime factors of a cube occur in multiples of three.

Thus $1728 = (2 \times 2 \times 2) \times (2 \times 2 \times 2) \times (3 \times 3 \times 3)$ is a cube and $432 = 2 \times (6 \times 6 \times 6)$ is not.

Divisibility by a composite number

Notice that every integer greater than 1 is either composite or prime; there is no other possibility.

To find whether or not an integer n is divisible by a composite number, use the prime factorisation of n.

For example, to see whether or not an integer is divisible by 15, it is sufficient to see whether or not the integer is divisible by 3 and by 5, since $15 = 3 \times 5$ and these are the *only* prime factors of 15.

Fact 15.3K

An integer is divisible by pq, where p and q are prime, when it is both divisible by p and divisible by q, and not otherwise.

However, this is just the simplest case, where there are only two prime factors. More generally, in order to see if an integer n is divisible by 360, say, you would see whether n is divisible by $8 = 2^3$, by $9 = 3^2$, and by 5—because $360 = 2^3 \times 3^2 \times 5$. This works because divisibility by 8, for example, includes divisibility by 4 and by 2.

Fact 15.3L

An integer is divisible by an integer n when it is divisible by the highest power of each prime in the prime factorisation of n, and not otherwise.

15.4   Placing digits

Questions that require the placement of digits are best solved using properties gleaned from the question rather than by working through a list. So make sure you know the number facts well.

Also, some constraints may narrow down the number of possible answers much more than others, so choose the order in which you work through them very carefully.

It is vital that you explain why you are choosing some possibilities and disregarding others.

For example, suppose you are solving a crossnumber and you know that the answer to a clue is to a two-digit integer which is both even and a multiple of five. You would be expected to explain why you were placing a zero in a certain box.

15.5   Fractions

Care should be taken whenever you are required to manipulate fractions. Remember that to multiply or divide fractions you do not need to have the same denominator.

For example,

$$\frac{2}{5} \times \frac{1}{3} = \frac{2 \times 1}{5 \times 3}$$

$$= \frac{2}{15}.$$

and

$$\frac{2}{5} \div \frac{1}{3} = \frac{2}{5} \times \frac{3}{1}$$

$$= \frac{2 \times 3}{5 \times 1}$$

$$= \frac{6}{5}.$$

However, when you add or subtract fractions, you should arrange for them to have the same denominator.

For example, to add $\frac{3}{10}$ and $\frac{1}{4}$, rewrite each fraction—without changing its value—so that both fractions have denominator 20 (the lowest common multiple of 10 and 4). Thus

$$\frac{3}{10} + \frac{1}{4} = \frac{3}{10} \times \frac{2}{2} + \frac{1}{4} \times \frac{5}{5}$$

$$= \frac{6}{20} + \frac{5}{20}$$

$$= \frac{11}{20}.$$

Remember that you cannot 'split' a denominator. For example, the following two fractions are very different:

$$\frac{1}{a+2} \quad \text{and} \quad \frac{1}{a} + \frac{1}{2}.$$

You should convince yourself of this by putting $a = 3$, say.

Working with mixed numbers

When working with mixed numbers, it is usually best to convert each mixed number to a fraction first, then convert back to a mixed number at the end.

For example,

$$4\tfrac{1}{3} - 1\tfrac{4}{7} = \frac{13}{3} - \frac{11}{7}$$

$$= \frac{13}{3} \times \frac{7}{7} - \frac{11}{7} \times \frac{3}{3}$$

$$= \frac{91}{21} - \frac{33}{21}$$

$$= \frac{58}{21}$$

$$= 2\tfrac{16}{21}.$$

The square root of a fraction

To take the square root of a fraction, you may take the square root of the numerator and the denominator separately.

For example,

$$\sqrt{\frac{5}{9}} = \frac{\sqrt{5}}{\sqrt{9}}$$

$$= \frac{\sqrt{5}}{3}.$$

15.6   Ratios

To divide a quantity in a specific ratio, first calculate the total number of parts into which the quantity is to be divided.

For example, to divide 70 in the ratio 3 : 2, there are $3 + 2 = 5$ parts altogether.

Therefore each part is $\frac{1}{5}$ of 70, so that each part is 14. Now $3 \times 14 = 42$ and $2 \times 14 = 28$, hence the parts are 42 and 28.

CHECK   By cancelling the ratio 42 : 28, you get the ratio 3 : 2, as required; and $42 + 28$ is 70, also as required.

15.7   Percentages

Whenever a quantity is increased or decreased by some percentage, it is often simpler to work with a multipying factor, making use of the fact that *per cent* means 'for each hundred'.

For example, suppose you want to increase something by 20%.

Now the result will be the original 100% with an extra 20% added on, which is 120%.

But $\frac{120}{100} = \frac{6}{5} = 1.2$, so in order to increase a quantity by 20%, multiply the original quantity by either $\frac{6}{5}$ or 1.2. Which of these exressions you use is likely to depend on the other numbers in the problem you are dealing with.

In the same way, in order to decrease a quantity by 15%, multiply the original quantity by either $\frac{17}{20}$ or 0.85, since $100\% - 15\% = 85\%$ and $\frac{85}{100} = \frac{17}{20} = 0.85$.

15.8   Speed, distance and time

Speed is the distance travelled in one unit of time, which leads to the following facts.

Fact 15.8A
$$speed = \frac{distance}{time}.$$

Fact 15.8B
$$distance = speed \times time.$$

Fact 15.8C
$$time = \frac{distance}{speed}.$$

Notice that phrases like 'travels at 6 mph' only make sense when the given speed is interpreted as the average speed. Indeed, the term 'speed' in facts 15.8A to 15.8C really means 'average speed'. On the majority of journeys in real life, you travel at different speeds during different parts of the journey, yet you are usually only interested in the overall distance and time.

Chapter 16

Algebra

Algebra is the branch of mathematics in which you use and manipulate symbols in order to help you to simplify a problem. Doing this also enables you to be certain that your answer is valid in all possible cases.

Some commonly used terms are defined in the glossary on page 255.

It often happens that a problem is posed in such a way that you can easily see one answer. But how are you to know that you have found all possible answers to that problem? One reason for using algebra is that doing so allows you to be certain.

16.1   Using letters to represent numbers

There are two important ways that you may introduce a letter to convert the language of words into the language of symbols:

(i) when you wish to use a specific property of the unknown;

(ii) when you wish to set up a relationship—most commonly in the form of an equation—between an unknown quantity and the known quantities.

For example, you might use $3k$, where k is an integer, to represent the multiples of 3, or you might use $\dfrac{n}{n+1}$ to represent fractions in which the denominator is 1 more than the numerator.

You should take care when introducing letters to represent numbers or digits. In mathematics, a symbol is used to describe a number—a quantity—and not a physical quality such as a length or a temperature.

> For example, if a question involves finding the number of tins of cocoa, then you would say 'let the number of tins be n' since your variable is the *number* of tins, and not the tins themselves.

When a letter is used to define the number or size of something, it is important to define any units at the start. By doing this, in mathematics you ensure that all your expressions connect *numbers*.

> For example, if the question is to find the length of a side, say 'let the length of the side be x *centimetres*'.

Introducing a letter to represent a particular unknown number in a given situation means that every possible case is considered. This enables you to know for certain that you have found every possible answer and that there are no others. Contrast this with using trial and error, or considering a few cases which work, where you have no way of knowing whether you have missed a possible answer.

> For example, suppose you were asked to find how many positive integers are
>
> (i) less than 10 000,
> (ii) 5 more than a multiple of 6, and also
> (iii) 4 more than a multiple of 7.
>
> Forming a list of all such integers would be quite demanding. However, if you consider what these integers look like, and use a little algebra, then you are a long way into solving the problem.
>
> Writing down the start of two lists may give an insight into how you might proceed.
>
> The positive integers which are 5 more than a multiple of 6 are
>
> $$11, 17, 23, 29, 35, 41, 47, 53, 59, 65, 71, 77, 83, 89, 95, 101, \ldots.$$

The positive integers which are 4 more than a multiple of 7 are

$$11, 18, 25, 32, 39, 46, 53, 60, 67, 74, 81, 88, 95, 102, \ldots.$$

Now the integers in common to both lists are 11, 54, 95, ..., that is, every seventh number in the first list and every sixth one in the second. But a number in the first list has the form $6k + 11$, for some integer k, and a number in the second list has the form $7m + 11$, for some integer m. Thus you can write an integer that is common to both lists as

$$6(7n) + 11, \text{ or as } 7(6n) + 11, \text{ for some integer } n.$$

But each of these expressions is equal to $42n + 11$, in other words, they are the same integer. Therefore any integer of the form $42n + 11$, where n is an integer, is common to both lists. Moreover, only integers of this form are.

Now $42n + 11$ has to be less than 10 000. But 42×243 is less than 10 000, and 42×244 is greater than 10 000. Hence n is at most 243.

Also, $42n + 11$ has to be positive, so that n is at least 0.

In other words, the integer n is between 0 and 243 (inclusive). But each value of n corresponds to a different value of the integer $42n + 11$. Hence you know, without any doubt, that there are 244 integers of the required form.

Note that, in the last example, the required integers have not been worked out—they were not asked for—yet the question has been completely answered.

As another example, suppose that the angles in a triangle are in the ratio 1 : 2 : 6, and that you are asked to find the largest angle.

A good start would be to let one of the angles in the triangle be $a°$. Notice that a is a number and the degrees are the unit of measurement.

Which angle should we choose? A useful rule of thumb is *let the unknown letter stand for whatever you are trying to find*, which would mean that we choose the largest angle here.

However, the algebra turns out to be slightly simpler if instead we work with the smallest angle. So a solution might read something like the following.

Let the smallest angle in the triangle be $a°$. Then the other two angles are $2a°$ and $6a°$.

Using the fact that the sum of the angles in a triangle is 180°, we get

$$a + 2a + 6a = 180,$$

so that

$$9a = 180$$

and hence

$$a = 20.$$

Now the largest angle is $6a°$, and therefore the required angle is 120°.

You need to be especially careful when you represent, say, a two-digit number by letters. The standard notation is to use single quote marks, so in this case 'ab' is used to represent an integer whose value is $10a + b$—it does not represent $a \times b$. When writing solutions to the problems in this book, you should be able to use such notation clearly and precisely.

Consecutive integers

Letters can be used to describe a set of consecutive integers.

For example, n and $n + 1$ are consecutive integers.

When dealing with an odd number of consecutive integers, it is often simpler to let n be the middle integer. This makes the total easier to work with. For example, the total of the five consecutive integers $n - 2$, $n - 1$, n, $n + 1$, $n + 2$ is $5n$, whereas the total of n, $n + 1$, $n + 2$, $n + 3$, $n + 4$ is $5n + 10$. Choosing the first method simplifies the arithmetic.

Now one of two consecutive integers is even and the other is odd, so they are $2k - 1$ and $2k$, or $2k$ and $2k + 1$. Representing the numbers in this way may be useful, say, if you need to consider even-odd relationships.

16.2   Solving equations

You can use equations as a tool to solve problems, by finding values which make the equation true.

For example, there is a unique answer to the equation $x = 4$ and two answers to the equation $x^2 = 4$, namely $x = 2$ and $x = -2$.

To solve an equation, it is usual to perform the same mathematical operation on each side of the equation. Normally the letters (the unknowns or variables) are kept on the left-hand side.

For example, to solve the equation $x + 4 = 7$, you may subtract 4 from each side to give $x + 4 - 4 = 7 - 4$, so that $x + 0 = 3$ and hence $x = 3$.

You could explain your solution by writing something like the following.

To solve the equation

$$x + 4 = 7.$$

Subtracting 4 from each side, we get

$$x = 7 - 4$$
$$= 3.$$

Here is a more complicated example.

For the equation $2x - 5 = \frac{1}{2}x + 13$ you might write out the solution as follows.

To solve the equation

$$2x - 5 = \tfrac{1}{2}x + 13.$$

Adding 5 to each side, we obtain

$$2x = \tfrac{1}{2}x + 18.$$

Subtracting $\tfrac{1}{2}x$ from each side, we now get

$$\tfrac{3}{2}x = 18$$

and so, multiplying each side by 2, we have

$$3x = 36.$$

Finally, dividing each side by 3, we obtain

$$x = 12.$$

Notice that, every time you perform the same action on *each* side of an equation, you should explain precisely what you are doing. This is partly what is meant by the instruction 'give full written solutions'.

Chapter 17

Geometry

Geometry is the branch of mathematics which deals with the properties of lines and shapes. At the level of the problems in this book, the shapes you will meet are usually triangles, squares and regular polygons. Therefore you really need to know and understand facts about the relationships between the angles and sides of such shapes.

Some commonly used terms are defined in the glossary on page 255.

Note that the shapes involved are taken to be *planar*—they lie in a flat surface, a plane—so 'a quadrilateral' means 'a plane quadrilateral'. But you should be alert to the possibility that, just occasionally, a shape may not lie in a plane, which makes things more complicated.

17.1 Diagrams

It is useful to draw a diagram carefully and think about lines and triangles as you build up this diagram. This often gives a good insight into how you might tackle the problem. However, a labelled diagram on its own is not sufficient, since then it is not clear how you have arrived at your answer.

Also, be very careful about how you label your diagram. Shapes are labelled 'cyclically'—the letters follow one another as you go round the shape—so that in figure 17.1 on the next page the square *ABCD* is labelled correctly, whereas in figure 17.2 it is not. The usual convention is that points are labelled anticlockwise.

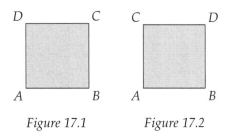

Figure 17.1   Figure 17.2

17.2 Angles

An *angle* is formed when two straight lines meet. Each line is called an *arm* and the point is called the *vertex* (figure 17.3).

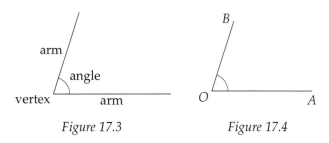

Figure 17.3   Figure 17.4

An angle is named by giving three letters with the vertex in the middle. Thus the angle with arms OA and OB is named $\angle BOA$ or $\angle AOB$ (figure 17.4). In this book, the convention is used that, where possible, geometrical shapes are named in an anticlockwise direction.

Three letters are used to describe an acute or an obtuse angle because this identifies the angle clearly. For a reflex angle, something like the following may be used to make clear that the angle is more than 180°: "The reflex angle XYZ is equal to ...".

There are some basic angle facts that you should know.

Fact 17.2A

The sum of the angles round a point is 360°.

Fact 17.2B

The sum of the angles on a straight line is 180°.

So in figures 17.5 and 17.6 it follows that $a + b + c + d = 360$ from fact 17.2A and $\alpha + \beta = 180$ from fact 17.2B.

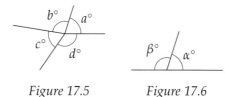

Figure 17.5   Figure 17.6

Fact 17.2C
  Vertically opposite angles are
  equal.

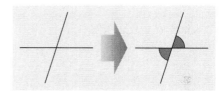

The *converse* of fact 17.2B is also true. (See the glossary on page 255 if you do not know the meaning of converse.)

Fact 17.2D
  If two angles share one arm and sum to 180°, then the other arms form a straight line.

So in figure 17.7, if $\gamma + \delta = 180$, then PQR is a straight line.

$$\gamma° \quad \delta°$$
$$P \quad Q \quad R$$

Figure 17.7

17.3   Parallel lines

Several pairs of equal angles are formed when two parallel straight lines are crossed by another straight line (known as a *transversal*).

Fact 17.3A
  Alternate angles on parallel
  lines are equal.

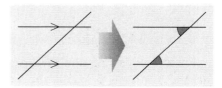

Fact 17.3B

*Corresponding angles on
parallel lines are equal.*

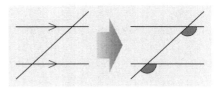

Fact 17.3C

*The sum of allied angles on
parallel lines is 180°.*

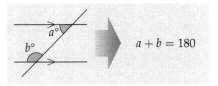

$a + b = 180$

There are also equivalent converse results, such as the following.

Fact 17.3D

*If corresponding angles on two
lines are equal, then the lines
are parallel.*

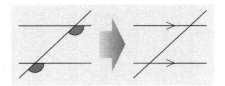

17.4   Triangles

Fact 17.4A

*The exterior angle of a triangle
is equal to the sum of the two
interior opposite angles.*

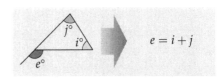

$e = i + j$

Fact 17.4B

*The sum of the angles in a
triangle is 180°.*

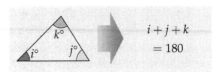

$i + j + k = 180$

Equilateral triangles

An equilateral triangle has three equal sides, and each of its three angles measures 60°. Every equilateral triangle has the same shape but not necessarily the same size.

Fact 17.4C
 A triangle is equilateral when one angle is equal to 60° and the arms of the angle are equal.

Any median in an equilateral triangle is the perpendicular bisector of the opposite side.

Isosceles triangles

A triangle is isosceles when it has two equal sides.

Fact 17.4D
 The angles opposite equal sides of a triangle are equal.

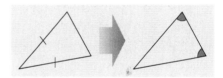

The converse result is also true:

Fact 17.4E
 The sides opposite equal angles of a triangle are equal.

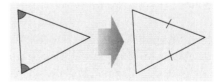

In answering a question, when you use either of these results, you should state the fact as a reason in your argument. Thus, for example in an isosceles triangle ABC in which $AB = BC$ you might say

Considering triangle ABC and using the angles opposite equal sides of a triangle are equal, we obtain $\angle CAB = \angle ACB$.

In an isosceles triangle, the two equal angles are sometimes called the *base angles*. The other angle is called the *vertex angle*.

Fact 17.4F

*The median through the vertex
angle of an isosceles triangle
meets the opposite side at right
angles.*

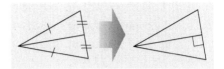

This follows because this median cuts the triangle into two identical (congruent) triangles. As a result of fact 17.4F, this median of an isosceles triangle is the *perpendicular bisector* of the opposite side.

Fact 17.4G

*The median through the vertex
angle of an isosceles triangle
bisects that angle.*

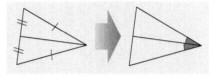

Right-angled isosceles triangles

The diagonal of a square bisects the square into two congruent isosceles triangles. Consider one such triangle (see figure 17.8).

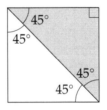

Figure 17.8

One angle in the triangle is 90°, since it is one of the angles of the square. Bisecting the angle at the vertex of a square gives two angles of 45°, so each of the other angles in the triangle is 45°.

Fact 17.4H

*Each base angle of a
right-angled isosceles triangle
is 45°.*

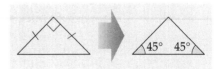

Congruent triangles

There are several ways of testing whether two triangles are congruent.

Fact 17.4I (The SSS test for congruency)
   If all three sides of one triangle have the same lengths as the sides of another triangle, then the two triangles are congruent.

Note that this result is false for general polygons, and is even false for quadrilaterals: for example, a square and a rhombus with the same side lengths need not be congruent.

Fact 17.4J (The AAS test for congruency)
   If a side and two angles of one triangle are equal to the corresponding side and angles of another triangle, then the two triangles are congruent.

act
.4B
106

Note that if two angles are equal, then the third angles will be equal from the fact that *the sum of the angles in a triangle is 180°.* However, it is still necessary to confirm that the positions of the sides correspond.

Fact 17.4K (The SAS test for congruency)
   If two sides of one triangle and the angle between them are equal to two sides of another triangle and the angle between them, then the two triangles are congruent.

Fact 17.4L (The RHS test for congruency)
   If two right-angled triangles have hypotenuses of the same length and one other side equal, then the triangles are congruent.

17.5   Polygons

The term polygon is usually used to refer to a *convex* shape, which means that all the vertices 'point outwards', as in figure 17.9.

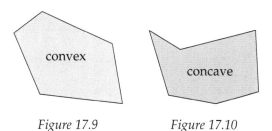

Figure 17.9   *Figure 17.10*

Suppose instead that the shape has one or more vertices 'pointing inwards', as in figure 17.10; then the polygon is *concave*. At least one of the interior angles of a concave polygon is a reflex angle. When referring to such a polygon, the fact that it is concave needs to be clearly stated.

The parallelogram

A parallelogram is a quadrilateral whose opposite sides are parallel. You should be familiar with the following basic properties of a parallelogram.

Fact 17.5A

The opposite sides of a parallelogram are equal in length.

Fact 17.5B

The opposite angles of a parallelogram are equal.

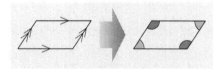

Fact 17.5C

A parallelogram is cut by a diagonal into two congruent triangles.

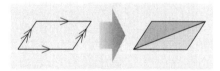

Fact 17.5D

The diagonals of a parallelogram bisect each other.

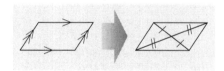

The rhombus

Formally, a rhombus is a parallelogram with two equal adjacent sides, but an equivalent definition—one that is more often used—is that a rhombus is a quadrilateral with four equal sides.

Since a rhombus is a parallelogram, it has the properties given in facts 17.5A to 17.5D. In addition, a rhombus has the following properties.

Fact 17.5E

> *A rhombus is dissected by the diagonals into four congruent triangles.*

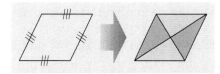

Fact 17.5F

> *The diagonals of a rhombus are perpendicular.*

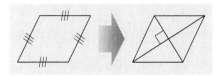

Facts 17.5D and 17.5F, taken together, show that each diagonal of a rhombus is the perpendicular bisector of the other.

Angles of a polygon

Figure 17.11 shows all the exterior angles of a polygon.

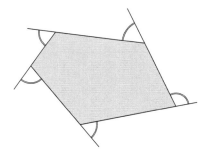

Figure 17.11

Suppose an ant traverses the boundary of the polygon once, travelling anticlockwise along the edges. At each vertex, the angle through which she turns is equal to the exterior angle at that vertex. But when the ant arrives back at her starting point, altogether she will have turned through 360°. This demonstrates the following fact.

Fact 17.5G

> *The sum of the exterior angles of any polygon is 360°.*

It is useful to know how to calculate the sum of the interior angles of any polygon. Let n be the number of sides of the polygon.

At each vertex, the sum of the exterior angle and the interior angle is 180°. Since there are n vertices, the sum of all the exterior angles and all the interior angles is therefore $n \times 180°$. But *the sum of the exterior angles of any polygon is 360°* (fact 17.5G on page 111). Therefore the sum of the interior angles may be found by subtracting 360° from $n \times 180°$, to get $n \times 180° - 360°$, which may be written in the form $(n - 2) \times 180°$.

Fact 17.5H

The sum of the interior angles of a polygon with n sides is $(n - 2) \times 180°$.

There are several other ways of deriving this result. For example, divide the polygon into triangles. One way to do this is to pick a vertex, then draw all the diagonals from that vertex (remember, we are assuming that the polygon is convex). This forms $n - 2$ triangles (can you see why?). Then use the fact that the sum of the angles in the triangles is the same as the sum of the interior angles of the polygon.

Angles of a regular polygon

When the polygon is regular, all the interior angles are equal in size, and thus all the exterior angles are equal in size. So the size of each exterior angle may be calculated by dividing the total given in fact 17.5G by the number of angles. But the number of angles is the same as the number of sides.

Fact 17.5I

The size of each exterior angle of a regular polygon with n sides is equal to $360° \div n$.

The simplest way to find the size of each interior angle is just to take the size of an exterior angle given by fact 17.5I and subtract from 180°. (Alternatively, take the total given by fact 17.5H and divide by n.)

> For example, the size of each exterior angle of a regular nonagon (a polygon with nine sides) is $360° \div 9 = 40°$. Therefore each interior angle has size $180° - 40° = 140°$.

17.6   Dissections

Two dissections that may be useful are of an equilateral triangle and a regular hexagon.

Fact 17.6A

> An equilateral triangle may be
> dissected into four equilateral
> triangles.

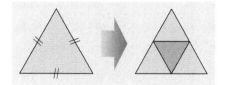

Fact 17.6B

> A regular hexagon may be
> dissected into six equilateral
> triangles.

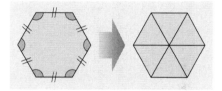

To obtain the dissection of an equilateral triangle, simply join the midpoints of the sides; for the regular hexagon, just join opposite vertices. In each case, the resulting small equilateral triangles are congruent.

Of course, it is necessary to show that these dissections are as described, in other words, that the small triangles are indeed equilateral. We may show, for example, that the darker triangle in figure 17.12 is equilateral, using fact 17.4C, because it has two equal sides and the marked angle is equal to 60°.

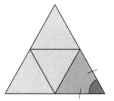

Figure 17.12

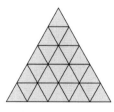

Figure 17.13

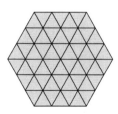

Figure 17.14

There are many other dissections of these two shapes into equilateral triangles. Figure 17.13 shows an equilateral triangle dissected into twenty-five triangles; figure 17.14 shows a regular hexagon dissected into fifty-four. However, it is tricky to *prove* that the small triangles in each figure are congruent.

17.7 Giving reasons

When you answer questions in geometry, it may be especially tempting just to assert that something is the case. You need to resist the temptation! Always give a reason for your claims.

For example, you might write

> Because $ABCD$ is a square, the diagonal CA bisects the angle at the vertex A of the square. Hence $\angle BAC = 45°$.

where the phrase 'Because $ABCD$ is a square' gives the reason for the statement that comes next.

In the same way, when answering a question in which you are using properties of parallel lines, you might write, for example,

> Using the sum of allied angles on parallel lines is 180°, we get $\angle PQR + \angle QRS = 180°$.

or, even better, also mention which lines are parallel:

> Because PQ and SR are parallel and the sum of allied angles on parallel lines is 180°, it follows that $\angle PQR + \angle QRS = 180°$.

This can only help someone trying to read your work, especially when your figure contains a lot of lines.

Similarly, when using a fact about triangles, it is good practice to mention which triangle you are working with. For example, you might write:

> In triangle ABC, using the exterior angle of a triangle is equal to the sum of the two interior opposite angles, we obtain . . . .

Chapter 18

Lengths and areas

Some commonly used terms are defined in the glossary on page 255.

Remember the advice about drawing diagrams in section 17.1 on page 103.

18.1 Scaling

When working with a regular polygon, it can be useful first to consider a polygon with sides of length 1 (or some other value that you are likely to find helpful). Any result you obtain can then be scaled in order to deal with a polygon of a different size.

> For example, the length of a diagonal of a regular hexagon with sides of length 1 is 2, therefore the length of a diagonal of a regular hexagon with sides of length 5 is 10.

As well as regular polygons, the idea of scaling may also be used for *any* triangle. We do so a couple of times below.

The scaling idea can be very useful—you can use scaling in order to work with a convenient side length.

18.2   Triangles

Area of a triangle

Fact 18.2A

The area of a triangle is equal to $\frac{1}{2} \times base \times height$.

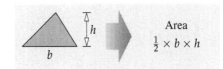

Area

$\frac{1}{2} \times b \times h$

One way to see this is to divide a rectangle with area $b \times h$ in the manner shown in figure 18.1. Can you see why this works? What should you do in figure 18.2?

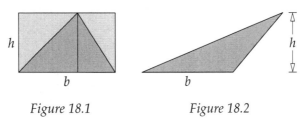

Figure 18.1	*Figure 18.2*

Right-angled triangles

In a right-angled triangle, the longest side—the one opposite the right angle—is known as the *hypotenuse.*

Fact 18.2B (Pythagoras' theorem)

In a right-angled triangle, the square of the hypotenuse is equal to the sum of the squares of the other two sides.

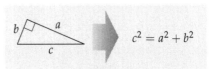

$c^2 = a^2 + b^2$

Pythagoras' theorem is one of the most important results you are likely to come across in mathematics. The *converse* result is also true. (See the glossary on page 255 if you do not know the meaning of converse.)

Fact 18.2C

If the lengths a, b and c satisfy $c^2 = a^2 + b^2$, then they are the side lengths of a right-angled triangle.

$c^2 = a^2 + b^2$

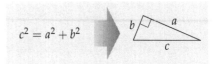

We may also determine the right angle: it is the angle opposite the side with longest length c.

Equilateral triangles

We may use Pythagoras' theorem to determine the relationship between the height of an equilateral triangle and the length of the sides.

Consider one of the right-angled triangles formed by a median in an equilateral triangle of side 2 (using *the median through the vertex angle of an isosceles triangle meets the opposite side at right angles* (fact 17.4F on page 108)). Then one side of this new triangle is of length 1 because the original side has been halved by the median. The hypotenuse is of length 2 and the third side can then be calculated using Pythagoras' theorem. Let the third side be of length h (figure 18.3).

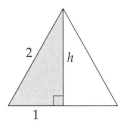

Figure 18.3

Then *Pythagoras' theorem* (fact 18.2B on page 116) applied to the shaded triangle gives

$$1^2 + h^2 = 2^2$$

and so

$$1 + h^2 = 4.$$

Subtracting 1 from each side, we get

$$h^2 = 3$$

and hence

$$h = \sqrt{3}$$

because h is positive.

Fact 18.2D

An equilateral triangle with sides of length 2 has height $\sqrt{3}$.

Using the idea discussed in "Scaling" on page 115, we may find the height of *any* equilateral triangle.

For example, suppose an equilateral triangle has sides of length 6. Then this triangle has sides that are three times the length of those in the triangle with sides of length 2. Therefore the height of the triangle is $3\sqrt{3}$.

The area of any equilateral triangle may be calculated from fact 18.2D, as long as the length of its side is known. Thus, using *the area of a triangle is equal to $\frac{1}{2} \times base \times height$* (fact 18.2A on page 116), the area of an equilateral triangle with sides of length 2 is

$$\tfrac{1}{2} \times 2 \times \sqrt{3} = \sqrt{3}.$$

Using the idea of scaling once more, to find the area of an equilateral triangle with sides of length 8, we multiply both the base and the height by 4. The area is therefore equal to

$$\tfrac{1}{2} \times \text{base} \times \text{height} = \tfrac{1}{2} \times 8 \times 4\sqrt{3}$$
$$= 16\sqrt{3}.$$

Right-angled isosceles triangles

Consider a unit square, that is, a square of side 1, and bisect it as described above. Then the third side of the triangle can be calculated using Pythagoras' theorem. Let the third side be of length h (see figure 18.4).

Then *Pythagoras' theorem* (fact 18.2B on page 116) applied to the shaded triangle gives

$$h^2 = 1^2 + 1^2$$
$$= 1 + 1$$
$$= 2$$

so that

$$h = \sqrt{2}$$

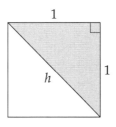

Figure 18.4

because *h* is positive.

The sides of the triangle are therefore 1, 1 and $\sqrt{2}$.

Using the idea discussed in "Scaling" on page 115, we deduce that when the equal sides of an isosceles right-angled triangle have length *s*, then the length of the hypotenuse is $\sqrt{2} \times s$.

3 : 4 : 5 triangles

Notice that $5^2 = 4^2 + 3^2$. From the result *if the lengths a, b and c satisfy $c^2 = a^2 + b^2$, then they are the side lengths of a right-angled triangle* (fact 18.2C on page 116), it follows that a triangle with sides 3, 4 and 5 is a right-angled triangle.

Similarly, a triangle with sides 6, 8 and 10 is right-angled; so is a triangle with sides 21, 28 and 35. Indeed, any triangle with side lengths in the ratio 3 : 4 : 5 is right-angled.

18.3   Circles

Fact 18.3A

> The length of the circumference of a circle with diameter *D* is equal to πD.

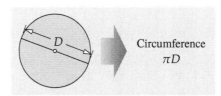

Fact 18.3B

The length of the circumference of a circle with radius r is equal to $2\pi r$.

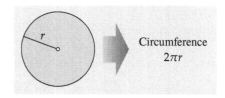

Fact 18.3C

The area of a circle of diameter D is equal to $\frac{1}{4}\pi D^2$.

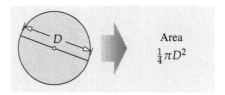

Fact 18.3D

The area of a circle of radius r is equal to πr^2.

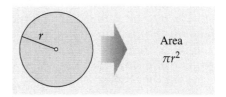

Chapter 19

Counting and reasoning

All mathematics involves logical reasoning, and when you write solutions to the problems in this book you should always be careful to use well-reasoned arguments.

After a discussion of counting, this chapter presents a few different kinds of reasoning that you ought to be aware of.

19.1   Counting

Some problems ask how many ways there are to carry out some task. Suppose you can break the task into stages, and you are able to count the number of ways there are to do each stage. But then how many ways are there when these stages are put together? The following rule helps.

Fact 19.1A (The multiplication principle)

Suppose there are m ways of making one choice and, whichever first choice is made, n ways of making a second choice. Then there are m × n ways of making both choices in succession.

> Suppose you want to find how many two-digit positive integers there are. Well, you know the answer: they are all the integers from 10 to 99, so there are $99 - 9 = 90$ of them.

However, there is another way to think about it. Consider a single digit d. Without any constraints, there are 10 choices for d, namely $0, 1, 2, 3, 4, 5, 6, 7, 8$ and 9.

So, in order to find the number of integers of the form 'tu' it is possible to reason as follows. There are 9 choices for the tens digit and for each of these 9 choices there are 10 possible units digits, and the choice is unaffected by the choice of the tens digit. This means that the total number of choices for 'tu' is $9 \times 10 = 90$, using the multiplication principle.

This may be extended to three or more digits. There are $900 = 9 \times 10 \times 10$ three-digit positive integers, since there are 9 choices for the hundreds digit, and 10 choices for each of the other two digits. We can generalise this to: there are $9 \times 10^{n-1}$ different n-digit positive integers.

The next example not only shows how to use fact 19.1A, but also illustrates the drawbacks of listing.

Suppose you are asked to find the number of triangles that can be drawn with each corner at one of the dots in the following figure.

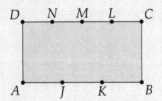

Several approaches are possible, and though all of the methods below are valid, they vary considerably in efficiency. We leave you to decide which of them you think is the most suitable.

Method 1

We attempt to find all the triangles by listing them systematically.

Let us try to create an alphabetical list, which will run from triangle ABC to triangle KMN. So we start with AB, join it to each of the other points in turn (alphabetically), and add any resulting triangles to the list. Then we repeat for BC, and so on. The resulting list is

$$ABC, ABD, ABL, ABM, ABN, BCD, BCJ, \ldots.$$

However, the list is rather long, and it is very easy to make a mistake—either to miss a triangle, or to include the same one twice. So this method is unlikely to give a correct answer; we shall not pursue it any further.

Method 2

We could consider the different types of triangles that may be made, and then find the number of triangles of each type. But first we have to decide what we mean by 'different types'. Let us say that two triangles are different when they have different angles.

Unfortunately, it is not clear how to go about finding the different types of triangle—there are a lot of angles to choose from—so it will be rather difficult to justify that any list is complete. For example, are triangles JKN and JLM different?

It is also going to be difficult to find how many triangles there are of each type.

Perhaps there is another way of giving a meaning to 'different types'? Though there are other possibilities the same difficulties always seem to apply, so we shall not continue with this method.

Method 3

Instead of thinking of triangles, we may count the number of ways of choosing the vertices. We choose 3 dots from 9. There are 9 ways of choosing the first dot, 8 for the second and 7 for the third. Using fact 19.1A, we obtain a total of $9 \times 8 \times 7 = 504$ ways. However, there are two difficulties with this:

(i) some choices of three points lie in a straight line, so do not form a triangle;

(ii) many triangles are counted more than once.

What we have actually done is count triples of labelled points, rather than triangles of dots. However, it is possible to redeem the situation.

The 'flat triangles'—where the three points lie in a straight line—are of two types. Either the three points lie along AB, or they lie along CD. Using fact 19.1A again, we obtain $4 \times 3 \times 2$ flat triangles along AB, and $5 \times 4 \times 3$ flat triangles along CD, making a total of $24 + 60 = 84$. This leaves $504 - 84 = 420$ 'proper' triangles.

Consider any triangle XYZ. It can be labelled in 6 different ways: XYZ, XZY, YXZ, YZX, ZXY and ZYX. This means that each triangle has been counted 6 times in total. So we need to divide by 6, thus getting $420 \div 6 = 70$ different triangles altogether.

Method 4

Once again we consider choosing points, but now we take into account where the points need to be in order to form a triangle.

Divide the nine points into two groups: those along AB; and those along CD. In other words, the groups are A, J, K, B and C, L, M, N, D. Then each triangle corresponds to choosing one point from one group and two from the other.

There are two cases: choose one point from the first group and two from the second; or *vice versa*.

Now there are 4 ways of selecting one point from the first group. Using fact 19.1A, there are $5 \times 4 = 20$ ways of selecting two points *in order* from the second group, so there are $20 \div 2 = 10$ ways when, as here, the order does not matter. Thus, using fact 19.1A again, in the first case we obtain $4 \times 10 = 40$ ways of choosing three points forming a triangle.

Using the same approach, in the second case we find that there are $5 \times 6 = 30$ ways. (We leave you to fill in the details.)

So altogether $40 + 30 = 70$ different triangles can be drawn.

19.2 'If' statements

You should know the difference between 'if A then B' and 'if B then A'.

For example, the statement

$$\boxed{\text{if } x = 2 \text{ then } x^2 = 4}$$

is *true*, whereas the statement

$$\boxed{\text{if } x^2 = 4 \text{ then } x = 2}$$

is *false* (because x might be -2).

19.3 Impossibility

To show that something is impossible can be demanding. One way to do this is to find an appropriate equation that you can prove is impossible to solve. Another way is to show that assuming a result to be true leads to an absurd answer.

In any case, proving that something is impossible requires precise logic and careful explanation.

For example, suppose you wish to show that it is impossible to find three integers greater than 1 that multiply together to give 10.

Because 2 and 5 are the *only* integers greater than 1 that multiply together to give 10, two of the numbers need to multiply together to give 2, or to give 5. Now both 2 and 5 are prime, and you cannot use 1 as one of the numbers, so this is not possible with integers.

Appendices

Appendix A

Solutions to the exercises

Solutions are given for all the problems in the exercises.

The solutions are not based on those given in the JMO booklets, and may well differ from them.

Exercise 4

1. (a) Let the top step use w blocks and let each remaining step use s blocks.

    > We introduce letters for the two unknowns that are mentioned in the question. Now we shall attempt to find some relationships—equations—connecting them. Apart from anything else, doing this means we can be certain that our solution gives all possible answers.

    Then, from the top, the number of blocks Kate uses at each level are w, $w + s$, $w + 2s$, $w + 3s$, $w + 4s$ and $w + 5s$.

    Altogether Kate uses 90 blocks, so we have

    $$w + (w + s) + (w + 2s) + (w + 3s) + (w + 4s) + (w + 5s) = 90.$$

    In other words,

    $$6w + 15s = 90.$$

Dividing each side by 3, we obtain

$$2w + 5s = 30.$$

Hence, subtracting $2w$ from each side, we get

$$5s = 30 - 2w. \tag{*}$$

Now the right-hand side of equation (*) is divisible by 2, so the left-hand side is divisible by 2. That is, $5s$ is divisible by 2. But 5 is not divisible by 2, so it follows that s is divisible by 2.

Since both s and w are positive and $2w + 5s = 30$, there are only two possibilities: $s = 2$, in which case $w = 10$; and $s = 4$, in which case $w = 5$.

CHECK   Six steps with widths 10, 12, 14, 16, 18 and 20 use 90 blocks in all; and six steps with widths 5, 9, 13, 17, 21 and 25 use 90 blocks in all. So each of these staircases is possible.

> Our method also shows that these are the *only* values that work.
>
> In general an equation like (*)—one equation with two unknowns—has an infinite number of solutions. But here w and s are positive integers; as a result the number of possibilities is finite.

(b) Suppose we could build a seven-step staircase.

For each of the first six levels, the same number of blocks would be used as before, that is, a total of $6w + 15s$ blocks. For the seventh level, $w + 6s$ blocks would be used. So now we have

$$(6w + 15s) + (w + 6s) = 90$$

so that

$$7w + 21s = 90. \tag{**}$$

The left-hand side of equation (**) is an integer that is divisible by 7. But the right-hand side is 90, which is not divisible by 7. Therefore it is *not* possible to build a seven-step staircase.

2. Let n be the number of 10p coins that Jenny has, and let m be the number of 50p coins that she has.

> At the start, it may look like we would require three letters for the unknowns. However, we can relate what would be the third unknown—the number of 20p coins Jenny has—to the other two, thereby reducing the amount of algebra involved.

Then the number of 20p coins she has is $20 - n - m$ since the total number of coins she has is 20.

The value of her 10p coins is $10n$ pence, the value of her 50p coins is $50m$ pence, and the value of her 20p coins, in pence, is $20 \times 20 - 20 \times n - 20 \times m = 400 - 20n - 20m$.

> We have used the fact that the total monetary value of each type of coin is the value of that particular coin multiplied by the number of coins of that type.

But the total value of all her coins is £5, which is 500p. Therefore we have

$$10n + 400 - 20n - 20m + 50m = 500$$

Collecting like terms and subtracting 400 from each side, we get

$$30m - 10n = 100.$$

Adding $10n$ to each side, we obtain

$$30m = 100 + 10n. \tag{1}$$

Finally, dividing by 10, we get

$$3m = 10 + n. \tag{*}$$

We are told that Jenny has more 50p coins than 10p coins. Hence m is greater than n. Therefore $3m$ is greater than $3n$. But $3m$ and $10 + n$ are the same, from equation (*), so that $10 + n$ is greater than $3n$. We can subtract n from each of these quantities to get 10 is greater than $2n$. It follows that n is less than 5.

Now n and m are positive integers, and we just found that n is less than 5. Putting n equal to 1, 3, or 4 in equation (*) does not give an integer value for m, but putting $n = 2$ does give an integer value for m.

When $n = 2$, we have $m = 4$ and $20 - n - m = 14$. Hence Jenny has two 10p coins, four 50p coins and fourteen 20p coins.

Check   Because $2 + 14 + 4 = 20$ there are indeed 20 coins, and 4 is greater than 2, so Jenny has more 50p coins than 10p coins. Also $2 \times 10 + 14 \times 20 + 4 \times 50 = 20 + 280 + 200$, which is 500, so the total value of the coins is £5.

> Our method also shows that these are the *only* values that work.

3. Let the first unknown integer be $12x$.

> Normally, we would use a single letter for the unknown, but here another approach leads to simpler algebra.
>
> Suppose we were to let the first integer be x. Then, as this is twice the second integer, the second integer would be $\frac{1}{2}x$. Similarly, the third integer would be $\frac{1}{3}x$ and the fourth would be $\frac{1}{4}x$. However, this involves fractions and makes the subsequent calculation rather awkward. We can avoid the fractions by multiplying by 12. That is, we choose to make the first integer equal to $12x$.

Dividing $12x$ by 2, 3 and 4 in turn gives the other integers as $6x$, $4x$ and $3x$.

Now the sum of the four integers is 400, so that

$$12x + 6x + 4x + 3x = 400,$$

and so, gathering terms,

$$25x = 400.$$

Hence, dividing both sides by 25, we obtain

$$x = 16.$$

Therefore four integers are $12 \times 16 = 192$, $6 \times 16 = 96$, $4 \times 16 = 64$ and $3 \times 16 = 48$.

Check   Each of 2×96, 3×64 and 4×48 is equal to 192. Also $192 + 96 + 64 + 48 = 400$, so these four integers do satisfy the given conditions.

> Our method actually shows that these are the only values that
> work.

4. Let the number of grapes Pierre grew in 2007 be p, then Alphonse grew $2p$ grapes in 2007.

Since the total of number of grapes Alphonse grew over the two years was 49 000, he grew $49\,000 - 2p$ grapes in 2008. But in that year Pierre grew twice as many grapes as Alphonse did, so the number of grapes that Pierre grew in 2008 was

$$2 \times 4900 - 2 \times p = 98\,000 - 4p.$$

Now Alphonse grew 49 000 grapes over the two years, so Pierre grew $49\,000 + 7600 = 56\,600$ grapes over the two years. Therefore

$$56\,600 = p + (98\,000 - 4p)$$
$$= 98\,000 - 3p$$

and so, adding $3p$ to each side, we obtain

$$3p + 56\,600 = 98\,000.$$

And now, subtracting 56 000 from each side gives

$$3p = 41\,400.$$

Dividing each side by 3, we get

$$p = 13\,800.$$

Thus Alphonse grew $2 \times 13\,800 = 27\,600$ grapes in 2007.

CHECK Alphonse grew 27 600 grapes in 2007. So Alphonse grew $49\,000 - 27\,600 = 21\,400$ grapes in 2008. Pierre grew $27\,600 \div 2 = 13\,800$ grapes in 2007 and $98\,000 - 4 \times 13\,800 = 42\,800$ grapes in 2008. We see that these values do satisfy all the conditions of the problem.

> Our method also shows that these are the *only* values that
> work.

5. Let the first term be a and let the second term be b.

The sequence of six numbers is therefore a, b, $a + b$, $a + 2b$, $2a + b$, $3a + 5b$.

> Note that the sequence is a *Fibonacci sequence* (see page 88), though knowing this does not help to solve the problem!

Now the fourth term is four times the first term, so that

$$3a + 5b = 4a$$

and so, subtracting $3a$ from each side

$$5b = a.$$

Thus we may write the sequence in terms of b only: $5b$, b, $6b$, $7b$, $13b$, $20b$.

> We *could* write the sequence in terms of a only, but that would involve fractions. By working in terms of b, we can avoid the fractions.

The sum of all six terms is 13, so that

$$5b + b + 6b + 7b + 13b + 20b = 13$$

and so

$$52b = 13.$$

Dividing both sides by 52, we get

$$b = \frac{13}{52}$$

$$= \frac{1}{4}.$$

Since $a = 5b$ it follows that $a = \frac{5}{4}$. Thus the first term is $\frac{5}{4}$.

CHECK   The last term in the sequence $\frac{5}{4}$, $\frac{1}{4}$, $\frac{6}{4}$, $\frac{7}{4}$, $\frac{13}{4}$, $\frac{20}{4}$ is four times the first term; and the sum of all six terms is

$$\frac{5 + 1 + 6 + 7 + 13 + 20}{4} = \frac{52}{4}$$

$$= 13.$$

Hence the conditions given in the question are satisfied.

6. Let the youngest child have age a months.

> We introduce a letter to represent the age that we are asked to find.

Then the age of the eldest child is $6a$ months. There are nine children, with eight gaps between their ages, so the eldest child is 8×15 months older than the youngest child. Therefore

$$6a = a + 8 \times 15,$$
$$= a + 120$$

and so, subtracting a from each side, we get

$$5a = 120.$$

Dividing each side by 5, gives

$$a = 24.$$

Hence the youngest child is 24 months old. In other words, the youngest child is 2 years old.

CHECK   The children ages are 2 years, 3 years and 3 months, 4 years and 6 months, 5 years and 9 months, 7 years, 8 years and 3 months, 9 years and 6 months, 10 years and 9 months, and 12 years. The oldest is indeed six times as old as the youngest.

> Our method also shows that these are the *only* values that work.

7. Let the two consecutive positive integers be n and $n + 1$, with n greater than 0.

> In choosing the form of these two integers, we have made use of the idea discussed in "Consecutive integers" on page 100. We do the same later when we select m.

The sum of these two integers is $2n + 1$, which is an odd integer, and is at least 3 (since n is at least 1).

Let the five positive consecutive integers be $m - 2$, $m - 1$, m, $m + 1$ and $m + 2$, with m greater than 2. The sum of these five integers is $5m$, which is a multiple of five, and is at least 15 (since m is at least 3).

Putting these two facts together, an integer satisfying both the given conditions is a multiple of 5, is odd, and is at least 15. But *an integer is divisible by 5 when the last digit is 0 or 5, and not otherwise*, and an integer whose last digit is 0 is even, not odd. So we require all the integers whose units digit is 5 that are less than 2013 and that are at least 15.

Fac
15.3
p 8

The first three such integers are 15, 25 and 35, and the last is 2005. How many integers are in this list?

> One way to answer that question would be to list all the nubers and count them. But there is another method, which is quicker and less prone to mistakes.

The gap between any two integers is 10, so altogether there are

$$\frac{2005 - 15}{10} + 1$$

integers—dividing the range by 10 gives the number of gaps, then we add 1 to get the number of integers.
But

$$\frac{2005 - 15}{10} = \frac{1990}{10}$$
$$= 199,$$

so altogether there are $199 + 1 = 200$ integers of the required form.

8. Let the unknown side of the square have length $5x$ cm.

> We choose $5x$ rather than x for our unknown simple to avoid having to use fractions.

Then each rectangle has length $5x$ cm and breadth x cm, as shown.

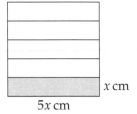

x cm

$5x$ cm

Now the perimeter of one rectangle is 51 cm, so that

$$5x + x + 5x + x = 51,$$

and so, gathering terms, we have

$$12x = 51.$$

Dividing both sides by 12, we get

$$x = \frac{51}{12}$$

$$= \frac{17}{4}.$$

Hence $5x = 5 \times \frac{17}{4}$, so that a side of the square has length $\frac{1}{4} \times 85$ cm and the perimeter has length $4 \times \frac{1}{4} \times 85$ cm $= 85$ cm.

CHECK   Five rectangles of length $\frac{17}{4}$ cm and breadth $\frac{85}{4}$ cm do indeed form a square of side $\frac{85}{4}$ cm.

> Our method also shows that these are the *only* values that work.

9. Let a be the unknown number in the top left hand cell. Then, from the information given in the question, the cells of the grid have the values shown in the following figure.

a	$2a$	$4a$
$3a$	$6a$	$12a$
$9a$	$18a$	$36a$

The sum of these nine numbers is $91a$. Hence we have

$$91a = 13.$$

Dividing both sides by 91, we obtain

$$a = \frac{13}{91}$$

and, noticing that $91 = 13 \times 7$, we get

$$a = \frac{1}{7}$$

Therefore the value of the number in the central cell is $6 \times \frac{1}{7} = \frac{6}{7}$.

CHECK   The following grid shows the resulting numbers in all the cells.

$\frac{1}{7}$	$\frac{2}{7}$	$\frac{4}{7}$
$\frac{3}{7}$	$\frac{6}{7}$	$\frac{12}{7}$
$\frac{9}{7}$	$\frac{18}{7}$	$\frac{36}{7}$

These numbers satisfy the given conditions.

> Our method also shows that these are the *only* values that work.

10. Let each card have short sides of length s units and long sides of length l units.

> We introduce two letters to represent the unknown lengths of the two sides of the rectangular card.

Then the perimeter of rectangle A, with short sides of the cards placed together, has length $6l + 2s$ units.

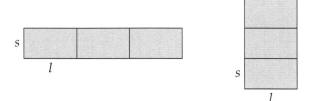

Also, the perimeter of rectangle B, with long sides of the cards placed together, has length $6s + 2l$ units. Twice this length is $12s + 4l$ units. This means that

$$12s + 4l = 6l + 2s.$$

Subtracting 2s from each side, we get
$$10s + 4l = 6l.$$
Subtracting 4l from each side, we obtain
$$10s = 2l.$$
Then dividing each side by 10, we get
$$s = \frac{2}{10}l$$
$$= \frac{1}{5}l.$$

Therefore the ratio of the length of a short side to the length of a long side is 1 : 5.

We have used the fact that one length is $\frac{1}{5}$ of the other, hence the ratio of the lengths is 1 : 5.

CHECK   Let the long side have length $5x$ units and the short side have length x units. Then rectangle A has length $15x$ units and breadth x units, so that the perimeter length is $15x + x + 15x + x$ units, which is equal to $32x$ units. Rectangle B has length $3x$ units and breadth $5x$ units, so that the perimeter length is $3x + 5x + 3x + 5x$ units, which is equal to $16x$ units. Thus the perimeter of rectangle A is twice that of rectangle B, as required.

Our method also shows that this is the *only* ratio that works.

Exercise 5

1.

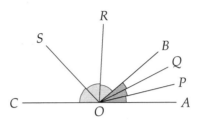

(a) Using *the sum of the angles on a straight line is 180°* for COA, we get $\angle COB + \angle BOA = 180°$, so that

$$\angle COB = 180° - \angle BOA$$
$$= 180° - 42°$$
$$= 138°$$

Since PO and QO trisect angle BOA, it follows that

$$\angle POA = \angle QOP = \angle BOQ$$

and each of them is equal to

$$\tfrac{1}{3} \times 42° = 14°.$$

Also, since RO and SO trisect $\angle COB$, it follows that

$$\angle ROB = \angle SOR = \angle COS$$

and each of them is equal to

$$\tfrac{1}{3} \times 138° = 46°.$$

Hence

$$\angle ROQ = \angle ROB + \angle BOQ$$
$$= 46° + 14°$$
$$= 60°,$$

and

$$\angle SOP = \angle SOR + \angle ROB + \angle BOQ + \angle QOP$$
$$= 46° + 46° + 14° + 14°$$
$$= 120°.$$

(b) When $\angle BOA = x°$, using the same method as in (a), we get
$$\angle BOQ = \tfrac{1}{3}x°.$$
Now
$$\angle BOA + \angle COB = 180°$$
and dividing each term by 3, we obtain
$$\tfrac{1}{3}\angle BOA + \tfrac{1}{3}\angle COB = \tfrac{1}{3} \times 180°$$
so that
$$\angle BOQ + \angle ROB = 60°$$
and hence
$$\tfrac{1}{3}x° + \angle ROB = 60°.$$
Subtracting $\tfrac{1}{3}x°$ from each side, we get
$$\angle ROB = 60° - \tfrac{1}{3}x°.$$
Therefore
$$\begin{aligned}\angle ROQ &= \angle ROB + \angle BOQ \\ &= (60° - \tfrac{1}{3}x°) + \tfrac{1}{3}x° \\ &= 60°.\end{aligned}$$

You may be wondering why x is not involved in the answer to (b).

Notice that
$$\angle BOA + \angle COB = 180°,$$
using *the sum of the angles on a straight line is 180°* (fact 17.2B on page 104). Therefore, dividing every term by 3, we get
$$\tfrac{1}{3}\angle BOA + \tfrac{1}{3}\angle COB = \tfrac{1}{3} \times 180°,$$
so that
$$\angle BOQ + \angle ROB = 60°.$$
Hence
$$\angle ROQ = 60°,$$
which does not depend on x.

So the size of $\angle BOA$ does not affect the size of $\angle ROQ$.

| This result provides a check of one of our answers in part (a). |

2.

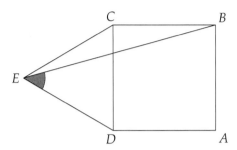

The figure shows the square and the equilateral triangle; we have also joined EB and marked the angle we want to find.

Now $ABCD$ is a square, therefore $AB = BC = CD = DA$. Also, triangle DCE is equilateral, therefore $DC = CE = ED$. As a result $BC = CE$, so that the triangle BCE has two equal sides and is isosceles.

Applying *the angles opposite equal sides of a triangle are equal* to triangle BCE, we therefore deduce that $\angle CEB = \angle EBC$.

Now $\angle BCD = 90°$ because it is the angle at a vertex of a square, and $\angle DCE = 60°$ because it is the angle at a vertex of an equilateral triangle. Hence $\angle BCE$, which is equal to $\angle BCD + \angle DCE$, is $90° + 60° = 150°$.

In triangle BCE, we may use *the sum of the angles in a triangle is 180°* to get

$$\angle CEB + \angle EBC + \angle BCE = 180°.$$

Substituting the results we obtained above, we get

$$\angle CEB + \angle CEB + 150° = 180°,$$

that is,

$$2 \times \angle CEB + 150° = 180°.$$

Subtracting $150°$ from each side, we obtain

$$2 \times \angle CEB = 180° - 150°$$
$$= 30°.$$

Thus, dividing each side by 2, we get

$$\angle CEB = 15°.$$

Finally, $\angle CED$ is equal to $60°$ since it is the angle at a vertex of an equilateral triangle. But

$$\angle CEB + \angle BED = \angle CED,$$

so that

$$15° + \angle BED = 60°$$

and therefore, subtracting $15°$ from each side, we obtain

$$\angle BED = 60° - 15°$$
$$= 45°.$$

3. Let the two pairs of equal angles be $a°$, $a°$ and $c°$, $c°$, and let $\angle ADC = d°$ and $\angle AEC = e°$, as shown.

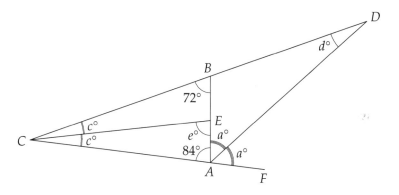

> We introduce some unknowns simply to help present the solution. Notice that we have been careful to include degrees, so that a, c, d and e are just numbers.

At A, using *the sum of the angles on a straight line is $180°$*, we get

$$a + a + 84 = 180$$

so that, subtracting 84 from each side, we have

$$2a = 96.$$

Dividing both sides by 2, we obtain

$$a = 48.$$

Then, using *the exterior angle of a triangle is equal to the sum of the two interior opposite angles* for $\triangle ABC$, we get

$$96 = 72 + 2c$$

so that, subtracting 72 from each side, we have

$$24 = 2c$$

Dividing both sides by 2, we obtain

$$12 = c$$

and hence

$$c = 12.$$

Thus $\angle DCA = 24°$.

Now using *the exterior angle of a triangle is equal to the sum of the two interior opposite angles* for $\triangle ADC$, we get

$$48 = 24 + d$$

so that, subtracting 24 from each side, we obtain

$$24 = d.$$

Therefore $\angle ADC = \angle DCA$, and we may use *the sides opposite equal angles of a triangle are equal* in $\triangle ADC$, to obtain $AD = CA$. If we can now prove that $CA = CE$ then we will have done.

Applying *the exterior angle of a triangle is equal to the sum of the two interior opposite angles* one last time, now for $\triangle AEC$, we get

$$96 = 12 + e$$

so that, subtracting 12 from each side, we obtain

$$84 = e.$$

Therefore $\angle AEC = \angle CAE$ and we may use *the sides opposite equal angles of a triangle are equal* in $\triangle AEC$, to obtain $CA = CE$.

It follows that $AD = CE$, as required.

4. Label the rhombus $ABCD$ and the triangle AXY, as shown in the following figure, where we have also marked the equal lengths.

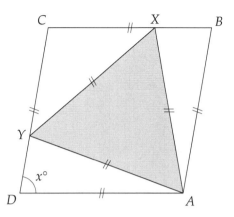

Now triangle AYD is isosceles with $AY = DA$, so using *the angles opposite equal sides of a triangle are equal*, we obtain $\angle AYD = \angle YDA$, so that $\angle AYD = x°$. Using *the sum of the angles in a triangle is 180°* in triangle AYD, we have

$$\angle DAY + \angle YDA + \angle AYD = 180°,$$

so that

$$\angle DAY + x° + x° = 180°$$

and hence

$$\angle DAY + 2x° = 180°.$$

Therefore, subtracting $2x°$ from each side, we get

$$\angle DAY = 180° - 2x°.$$

Since a rhombus is a parallelogram, we conclude from *the opposite angles of a parallelogram are equal* that $\angle ABC = \angle CDA = x°$.

Now triangle ABX is isosceles with $AB = XA$, so using *the angles opposite equal sides of a triangle are equal* once again, we obtain $\angle BXA = \angle ABX$, so that $\angle BXA = x°$.

Using precisely the same method as we used above to find $\angle DAY$, we get $\angle XAB = 180° - 2x°$.

Since $\angle YAX$ is the angle at a vertex of an equilateral triangle it is equal to $60°$. Hence we have

$$\angle DAB = \angle DAY + \angle YAX + \angle XAB$$
$$= (180° - 2x°) + 60° + (180° - 2x°)$$
$$= 420° - 4x°.$$

However, DC and AB are opposite sides of a rhombus and are therefore parallel, so we may use *the sum of allied angles on parallel lines is 180°* to obtain

$$180 = x + (420 - 4x)$$
$$= x + 420 - 4x$$
$$= 420 - 3x.$$

Dividing each term by 3, we get

$$60 = 140 - x.$$

Then, adding x to each side, we obtain

$$x + 60 = 140$$

and therefore, subtracting 60 from each side, we have

$$x = 80.$$

5.

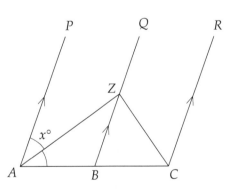

(a) We are given that ZA bisects $\angle PAB$ and so

$$\angle ZAB = \angle PAZ$$
$$= x°.$$

act
7.3A
105

Also, PA is parallel to ZB, so using *alternate angles on parallel lines are equal*, we obtain

$$\angle BZA = \angle PAZ$$

so that

$$\angle BZA = x°.$$

Now $\angle CBZ$ is an exterior angle of triangle ABZ and so, using *the exterior angle of a triangle is equal to the sum of the two interior opposite angles*, we get

act
.4A
106

$$\angle ZBC = \angle BZA + \angle ZAB$$
$$= x° + x°$$
$$= 2x°.$$

(b) We have shown that triangle ZAB has two equal angles and so, using *the sides opposite equal angles of a triangle are equal*, we deduce that

$$AB = BZ.$$

act
.4E
107

But we are given that B bisects AC, in other words, $AB = BC$. It follows that $BC = ZB$.

Hence triangle ZBC has two equal sides. Thus, using *the angles opposite equal sides of a triangle are equal*, we have

nct
4D
.07

$$\angle BCZ = \angle CZB.$$

However, BZ is parallel to CR and therefore, using *alternate angles on parallel lines are equal*, we obtain

ct
3A
05

$$\angle ZCR = \angle CZB$$
$$= \angle BCZ$$

Thus $\angle ZCR = \angle BCZ$ and so ZC bisects $\angle BCR$.

6. Let $\angle XBC = x°$. Then $\angle AXY = 7x°$.

Since $\angle XYA = \angle BCA$ (we are given that each of them is equal to $90°$) we conclude that BC and XY are parallel, from the result *if corresponding angles on two lines are equal, then the lines are parallel*.

ct
3D
06

Next, we extend BX to Z, as shown in the following figure.

Note that it is not necessary to extend BX; the problem may be solved in more standard ways, for example, by 'chasing angles' round the original figure.

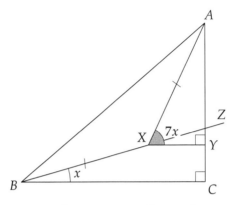

Then $\angle ZXY = \angle XBC$, from *corresponding angles on parallel lines are equal*. Hence $\angle AXZ = 7x° - x°$, which is $6x°$.

Now consider triangle ABX. Since $BX = XA$, it follows from *the angles opposite equal sides of a triangle are equal* that $\angle XAB = \angle ABX$. Using *the exterior angle of a triangle is equal to the sum of the two interior opposite angles*, we obtain

$$\angle XAB + \angle ABX = \angle AXZ,$$

so that

$$\angle XAB + \angle XAB = \angle AXZ$$

and hence

$$2 \times \angle XAB = 6x°.$$

Dividing both sides by 2, we get

$$\angle XAB = 3x°.$$

But XA bisects $\angle CAB$, so that $\angle YAX = \angle XAB$ and so $\angle YAX = 3x°$. Using *the sum of the angles in a triangle is 180°* in triangle AXY, we get

$$3x + 7x + 90 = 180,$$

so that, gathering terms and subtracting 90 from each side, we have

$$10x = 90.$$

Dividing both sides by 10, we obtain

$$x = 9.$$

Finally, we have

$$\begin{aligned}
\angle ABC &= \angle ABX + \angle XBC \\
&= 3x° + x° \\
&= 4x° \\
&= 4 \times 9° \\
&= 36°.
\end{aligned}$$

7. Join R to D and consider triangle RAD, shown shaded in the figure.

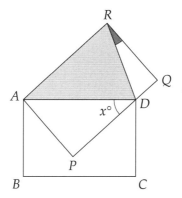

Because opposite sides of a rectangle are parallel, PD is parallel to RA. Therefore, using *alternate angles on parallel lines are equal*, we get $\angle RAD = \angle PDA$, and so $\angle RAD = x°$.

Rectangles $ABCD$ and $APQR$ are identical (congruent), so that AD and RA are equal in length. Thus triangle DRA is isosceles. We deduce that $\angle DRA = \angle ADR$, using *the angles opposite equal sides of a triangle are equal*.

Now we apply *the sum of the angles in a triangle is 180°* to triangle RAD to obtain

$$\angle DRA + \angle ADR + \angle RAD = 180°,$$

so that

$$\angle DRA + \angle DRA + x° = 180°$$

and hence, gathering terms and subtracting x from each side, we obtain

$$2 \times \angle DRA = 180° - x°.$$

Dividing both sides by 2, we get

$$\angle DRA = 90° - \tfrac{1}{2}x°.$$

But $\angle QRA = 90°$ because it is the angle at a vertex of a rectangle. Hence

$$\angle QRD + \angle DRA = 90°,$$

that is,

$$\angle QRD + 90° - \tfrac{1}{2}x° = 90°$$

and therefore, adding $\tfrac{1}{2}x°$ to each side, we obtain

$$\angle QRD + 90° = 90° + \tfrac{1}{2}x°$$

and, subtracting 90° from each side, we finally get

$$\angle QRD = \tfrac{1}{2}x°.$$

8.

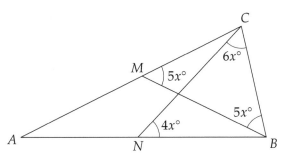

Applying *the sum of the angles in a triangle is 180°* to triangle BCM, we get

$$\angle BCM + \angle CMB + \angle MBC = 180°,$$

so that

$$\angle BCM + 5x° + 5x° = 180°$$

and hence, subtracting $10x$ from each side, we obtain

$$\angle BCM = 180° - 10x°.$$

Applying *the sum of the angles in a triangle is 180°* to triangle BCN, we get

$$\angle BCN + \angle CNB + \angle NBC = 180°,$$

so that

$$6x° + 4x° + \angle NBC = 180°$$

and hence, subtracting $10x$ from each side, we obtain

$$\angle NBC = 180° - 10x°.$$

So angles ABC and BCA are equal, because each of them is equal to $180° - 10x°$.

Therefore, applying *the sides opposite equal angles of a triangle are equal*, we get $AB = CA$ and so triangle ABC is isosceles.

Exercise 6

1. Since 200 is even it follows that either exactly one of p, q or r is even, or all three are even. However, 2 is the only even prime number and $2 + 2^2 + 2^3 = 14$, not 200, so it is impossible for all of p, q and r to be equal to 2.

Therefore, exactly one of p, q or r is equal to 2. Let us consider each case in turn.

$p = 2$

When $p = 2$ we have

$$2 + q^2 + r^3 = 200$$

so that

$$q^2 + r^3 = 198. \tag{1}$$

But $6^3 = 216$, so that r is less than 6. For each prime r greater than 2 and less than 6, we can use equation (1) to find the corresponding value of q^2.

r	q^2
3	171
5	73

In neither case is the value of q^2 a square, so there is no integer value of q. Hence there are no ways to write 200 in the required form when $p = 2$.

$q = 2$

When $q = 2$ we have

$$p + 2^2 + r^3 = 200,$$

so that

$$p + 4 + r^3 = 200.$$

Subtracting 4 from each side, we obtain

$$p + r^3 = 196. \tag{2}$$

But $6^3 = 216$, so that r is less than 6. For each prime r greater than 2 and less than 6, we can use equation (2) to find the corresponding value of p, and then decide whether or not the resulting value of p is prime.

r	p	Is p prime?	Reason
3	169	no	$169 = 13 \times 13$
5	71	yes	not divisible by 2, 3, 5 or 7

Thus when $q = 2$ there is only one possible way to write 200 in the required form, namely $71 + 2^2 + 5^3$.

$r = 2$

When $r = 2$ we have

$$p + q^2 + 2^3 = 200,$$

so that

$$p + q^2 + 8 = 200.$$

Subtracting 8 from each side, we get

$$p + q^2 = 192. \tag{3}$$

But $14^2 = 196$, so that q is less than 14. For each prime q greater than 2 and less than 14, we can use equation (3) to find the corresponding value of p, and then decide whether or not the resulting value of p is prime.

> Using the idea discussed in "Primes" on page 89, in order to establish whether a number is prime we only need to check for potential prime divisors up to the square root of the number.

q	p	Is p prime?	Reason
3	183	no	$183 = 3 \times 61$
5	167	yes	not divisible by 2, 3, 5, 7 or 11
7	143	no	$143 = 11 \times 13$
11	71	yes	not divisible by 2, 3, 5 or 7
13	23	yes	not divisible by 2 or 3

Three of the values of p are prime, so when $r = 2$ there are three possible ways to write 200 in the required form.

Therefore altogether there are four ways to write 200 in the required form:

$$71 + 2^2 + 5^3, \ 23 + 13^2 + 2^3, \ 71 + 11^2 + 2^3 \text{ and } 167 + 5^2 + 2^3.$$

2. (a) The fourth term of the sequence is

$$\frac{1}{2} - \frac{1}{3} + \frac{1}{4} = \frac{6}{12} - \frac{4}{12} + \frac{3}{12}$$

$$= \frac{5}{12}.$$

The fifth term is

$$\frac{5}{12} - \frac{1}{2} + \frac{1}{3} = \frac{5}{12} - \frac{6}{12} + \frac{4}{12}$$

$$= \frac{3}{12}$$

$$= \frac{1}{4}.$$

The sixth term is

$$\frac{1}{4} - \frac{5}{12} + \frac{1}{2} = \frac{3}{12} - \frac{5}{12} + \frac{6}{12}$$

$$= \frac{4}{12}$$

$$= \frac{1}{3}.$$

Hence the first six terms are

$$\frac{1}{4}, \frac{1}{3}, \frac{1}{2}, \frac{5}{12}, \frac{1}{4}, \frac{1}{3}.$$

(b) Continuing the calculations, the seventh term is

$$\frac{1}{3} - \frac{1}{4} + \frac{5}{12} = \frac{1}{2}$$

Hence the first seven terms of the sequence are

$$\frac{1}{4}, \frac{1}{3}, \frac{1}{2}, \frac{5}{12}, \frac{1}{4}, \frac{1}{3}, \frac{1}{2}$$

and we observe that the fifth, sixth and seventh terms are identical to the first three terms. Because each later term in the sequence depends only on the three previous ones, this means that the terms in the sequence form a repeating cycle of length four, repeating the values

$$\frac{1}{4}, \frac{1}{3}, \frac{1}{2}, \frac{5}{12}.$$

> We need to do more than observe that a finite number of terms of the sequence repeats—which is just spotting a pattern—it is essential to explain how we know that the sequence will repeat *for ever*.

Now $10 = 4 \times 2 + 2$, so the tenth term is equal to the second term, which is $\frac{1}{3}$.

Also, $100 = 4 \times 25$ and so the 100th term is the same as the fourth term, which is $\frac{5}{12}$.

3. The smallest integer will have the smallest number of digits. Therefore, each of these digits should be as large as possible. The largest possible digit is 9.

Now dividing 2015 by 9 leaves a remainder of 8. Therefore N is the positive integer whose leftmost digit is 8 and every other digit is 9. So the number N is 8 followed by a string of 9s.

Thus the leftmost digit of $N + 1$ is 9 and every other digit is 0, that is, $N + 1$ is the number 9 followed by a string of 0s. Hence the sum of the digits of $N + 1$ is 9.

> It is possible to find the actual value of N, using the fact that $2015 \div 9 = 223$ with remainder 8, but this is not necessary.

4. Let us start with the clue for 1 ACROSS.

> There is only a small number of two-digit squares, so starting with 1 ACROSS makes sense, especially when we combine it with the down clues.

The two-digit squares are 16, 25, 36, 64 and 81.

However, from the clue for 1 Down, the leading digit of 1 Down is the first digit of a cube. The three-digit cubes are $5^3 = 125$, $6^3 = 216$, $7^3 = 343$, $8^3 = 512$ and $9^3 = 729$. None of these begins with 6 or 8, so that 64 and 81 can be discarded as options for 1 Across. This leaves three possibilities:

	¹1	²6			¹2	²5			¹3	²6
³	2			³	1			³	4	
⁴	5			⁴	6			⁴	3	

Consider 2 Down in the middle diagram. No two-digit square starts with a 5, so that the middle diagram is not possible.

Consider 4 Across in the right-hand diagram. No two-digit square ends with a 3, so that the right-hand diagram is not possible either.

For the left-hand diagram, there is only one possibility for each of 2 Down and 4 Across, so that we have:

	¹1	²6
³	2	4
⁴2	5	

Now 3 Across is a three-digit square with units digit 4. Therefore, the units digit of the original integer has units digit 2 or 8.

Also, $32^2 = 1024$ and so we need only consider the two-digit integers 12, 18, 22 and 28 as those to be squared. The only possibility is 18, since none of $12^2 = 144$, $22^2 = 484$ or $28^2 = 784$ has 2 in the tens position, whereas $18^2 = 324$ does.

This completes every cell of the crossnumber, as shown:

	¹1	²6
³3	2	4
⁴2	5	

However, we have not used one clue. We need to confirm that the values we have obtained agree with this clue.

The unused clue is 3 DOWN. But 32 is equal to $8 \times 4 = 2^3 \times 2^2$, which is a cube times a square, so that the values we have obtained also fit this clue.

We have found one solution to the crossnumber, and our method shows that it is the only possible solution. Therefore there is exactly one solution to the crossnumber.

5. Using the fact that *the sum of the integers from 1 to n is equal to* $\frac{1}{2}n(n + 1)$, we know that the sum of the integers from 1 to 10 is $\frac{1}{2} \times 10 \times 11 = 55$.

There are five lines each with a sum of T and so the total of the five lines is $5 \times T = 5T$. Each of the five 'corner' integers appear in two lines, so each is counted twice in this calculation.

Let c be the missing corner integer. Then the five corner integers have a total of $c + 3 + 4 + 7 + 10 = c + 24$. Thus we have

$$5T = 55 + 24 + c,$$

so that

$$5T = 79 + c.$$

Now the left-hand side of this equation is divisible by 5, so the right-hand side is divisible by 5.

Remembering that c is a number between 1 and 10, the only possibilities for c are 1 and 6, so that either $5T = 80$ or $5T = 85$. The corresponding values of T are 16 and 17.

We may now complete the diagram for each of $T = 16$ and $T = 17$.

When $T = 16$, we know that $c = 1$. Then all the integers midway along each edge are determined, as shown in figure A on the following page. Since all the numbers from 1 to 10 are included, this is a valid solution.

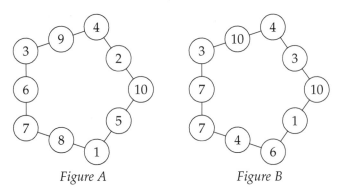

Figure A   *Figure B*

When $T = 17$, we know that $c = 6$. Then all the integers midway along each edge are determined, as shown in figure B. But in this case several integers are repeated, so this is not a valid solution.

Hence there is only one possible value of T, namely 16.

6. Let us start with 1 Down.

> There are only four clues to choose from, but 1 Down has the smallest number of possible answers.

The two-digit multiples of 25 are 25, 50 and 75. However, 50 cannot be used, otherwise 3 Across would begin with a zero. Therefore 1 Down is 25 or 75.

Now consider 3 Across. We now know that 3 Across begins with 5. The multiples of 3 that have a 5 in the tens position are $51 = 3 \times 17$, $54 = 3 \times 18$ and $57 = 3 \times 19$. However, 18 is not prime so 54 is excluded. Thus 3 Across is 51 or 57.

Next, consider 2 Down. we now know that the units digit is 1 or 7. But there are no squares with units digit 7, and the only two-digit square with 1 as the units digit is 81. Therefore 2 Down is 81, and so 3 Across is 51.

^{1}2	^{2}8
^{3}5	1

^{1}7	^{2}8
^{3}5	1

Finally, consider 1 ACROSS. We now know that it is either 28 or 78. But 28 is not a multiple of 3, whereas $78 = 26 \times 3$, so 78 is a multiple of 3. Therefore 1 ACROSS is 78, and so 1 DOWN is 75.

Hence there is a unique solution, as shown below.

^{1}7	^{2}8
^{3}5	1

7. The distance is the same for each journey. Therefore, from the fact that *distance = speed × time*, we know in each part that speed × time is the same for each journey.

(a) The new time is 25% more than the old time, so

$$\text{new time} = 1.25 \times \text{old time}$$

because $100\% + 25\% = 125\%$, which is $\frac{125}{100} = 1.25$ (making use of the method described in "Percentages" on page 94).

Considering speed × time for each journey, we get

$$\text{new speed} \times 1.25 \times \text{old time} = \text{old speed} \times \text{old time}.$$

Hence, dividing each side by 'old time' (which is not zero), we obtain

$$\text{new speed} \times 1.25 = \text{old speed}.$$

Multiplying each side by 0.8, we get

$$\text{new speed} = 0.8 \times \text{old speed}$$
$$= 80\% \times \text{old speed}.$$

Therefore the average speed has reduced by $100\% - 80\% = 20\%$.

(b) The time has decreased by 20%, so that

$$\text{new time} = 0.8 \times \text{old time}$$

because $100\% - 20\% = 80\%$, which is $\frac{80}{100} = 0.8$ (using the method described in "Percentages" on page 94).

Considering speed × time for each journey, we get

$$\text{new speed} \times 0.8 \times \text{old time} = \text{old speed} \times \text{old time}$$

On dividing each side by 'old time' (which is not zero), we obtain

$$\text{new speed} \times 0.8 = \text{old speed}.$$

Multiplying each side by 1.25, we get

$$\text{new speed} = 1.25 \times \text{old speed}$$
$$= 125\% \times \text{old speed}.$$

Therefore the average speed has increased by 25%.

8. Tom's speed was 60 mph, so that he travelled 60 miles in 60 minutes, that is, Tom travelled 1 mile in every minute. He travelled for a total time of 1 hour and 50 minutes, which is 110 minutes. In that time he therefore covered a distance of 110 miles.

   Tim covered the same distance in 1 hour and 40 minutes, which is 100 minutes.

   So Tim covered 110 miles in 100 minutes, so that he travelled every 11 miles in 10 minutes. Hence Tim would cover a distance of 66 miles in 60 minutes. In other words, Tim travelled at 66 mph.

9. The largest three-digit integer is 999, so that the sum of two three-digit integers is at most $999 + 999 = 1998$. Hence S can only be 1. We therefore have the following.

$$\begin{array}{r} J\,M\,C \\ +\ J\,M\,O \\ \hline 1\,U\,M\,1 \end{array}$$

We conclude that J is at least 5.

Next we consider the 'units' column. We have either $C + O = 1$ or $C + O = 11$. But no two letters stand for the same digit, and 1 has already been used, so the first case is impossible. Therefore $C + O = 11$ and there is a 'carry' of 1 to the 'tens' column.

Now consider the 'tens' column. We have either $M + M + 1 = M$ or $M + M + 1 = M + 10$, depending on whether there is a 'carry'. The first case is impossible, and in the second case $M = 9$. We therefore have the following.

$$
\begin{array}{r}
J\;9\;C \\
+\;J\;9\;O \\
\hline
1\;U\;9\;1
\end{array}
$$

Finally, we consider the 'hundreds' column. We know that J is at least 5. But $J = 5$ is impossible, because then U would be equal to 1, which has already been used. Also $J = 9$ is impossible, because 9 has already been used. That leaves three cases, $J = 6$, $J = 7$ and $J = 8$, as shown in the following figures.

$$
\begin{array}{r}
6\;9\;C \\
+\;6\;9\;O \\
\hline
1\;3\;9\;1
\end{array}
\qquad
\begin{array}{r}
7\;9\;C \\
+\;7\;9\;O \\
\hline
1\;5\;9\;1
\end{array}
\qquad
\begin{array}{r}
8\;9\;C \\
+\;8\;9\;O \\
\hline
1\;7\;9\;1
\end{array}
$$

Let us consider the possible values of J in turn, remembering that $C + O = 11$, and that different letters stand for different digits.

$J = 6$
The only possibilities for C and O are 4 and 7 (in either order).

$J = 7$
The only possibilities for C and O are 3 and 8 (in either order).

$J = 8$
The only possibilities for C and O are 5 and 6 (in either order).

So altogether there are six solutions, shown below.

$$
\begin{array}{r}
6\;9\;4 \\
+\;6\;9\;7 \\
\hline
1\;3\;9\;1
\end{array}
\quad
\begin{array}{r}
6\;9\;7 \\
+\;6\;9\;4 \\
\hline
1\;3\;9\;1
\end{array}
\quad
\begin{array}{r}
7\;9\;3 \\
+\;7\;9\;8 \\
\hline
1\;5\;9\;1
\end{array}
\quad
\begin{array}{r}
7\;9\;8 \\
+\;7\;9\;3 \\
\hline
1\;5\;9\;1
\end{array}
\quad
\begin{array}{r}
8\;9\;5 \\
+\;8\;9\;6 \\
\hline
1\;7\;9\;1
\end{array}
\quad
\begin{array}{r}
8\;9\;6 \\
+\;8\;9\;5 \\
\hline
1\;7\;9\;1
\end{array}
$$

10. The two-digit triangular numbers (see page 85) are

$$10,\ 15,\ 21,\ 28,\ 36,\ 45,\ 55,\ 66,\ 78 \text{ and } 91. \tag{*}$$

Consider 2 Down.

> Of the four clues, 2 Down is the one with the smallest number
> of possibilities for the units digit.

2 Down is a multiple of 5, so the units digit is 0 or 5. Hence the units digit of 3 Across is 0 or 5.

Now consider 3 Across. The units digit is 0 or 5. From the list (*), the only triangular numbers whose units digit is 0 or 5 are 10, 45 and 55. So the only possibilities for 3 Across are 10, 45 and 55.

Suppose that 3 Across is 10. Then the bottom left-hand cell is 1 and the only two-digit square with units digit 1 is 81, so 1 Down is 81. However, from the list (*), there is no triangular number whose first digit is 8, meaning that there is no answer to 1 Across. Hence 10 cannot be the answer to 3 Across. Thus 3 Across is either 45 or 55.

Thus the units digit of 1 Down is 4 or 5. But 64 is the only two-digit square with units digit 4, and 25 is the only two-digit square with units digit 5.

So far, we therefore have two possibilities, as follows.

^{1}6	^{2}
^{3}4	5

^{1}2	^{2}
^{3}5	5

Now consider 1 Across. Referring to the list (*), we may place appropriate triangular numbers to obtain the following three possible solutions.

^{1}6	^{2}6
^{3}4	5

^{1}2	^{2}1
^{3}5	5

^{1}2	^{2}8
^{3}5	5

Hence the crossnumber may be completed in three ways.

CHECK   For each of these solutions, each clue is correct, and our method shows that no other placement of digits is possible.

Exercise 7

1. Since $15 = 3 \times 5$, the integer N is divisible by 15 when it is divisible both by 3 and by 5, and not otherwise, using the fact that *an integer is divisible by pq, where p and q are prime, when it is both divisible by p and divisible by q, and not otherwise.*

   Let the leading digit of the four-digit integer be a and the units digit be b, so that the integer is '$a12b$'.

   Now the required integer is divisible by 5, so that b is 0 or 5 (from the fact that *an integer is divisible by 5 when the last digit is 0 or 5, and not otherwise*).

   We consider these two cases in turn.

   $b = 0$

   In this case $N = $ '$a120$'. Since N is divisible by 3, the sum of its digits is divisible by 3 (from the fact that *an integer is divisible by 3 when the sum of the digits is divisible by 3, and not otherwise*). But $1 + 2 + 0 = 3$, therefore a is a multiple of 3. That is, a is 0, 3, 6 or 9 (remembering that a is a digit). However, a four-digit integer cannot start with 0 and thus we obtain three answers: 3120, 6120 and 9120.

   $b = 5$

   In this case $N = $ '$a125$'. Once again, the sum of the digits of N is divisible by 3. But $1 + 2 + 5 = 8$, therefore a is one more than a multiple of 3. That is, a is 1, 4 or 7 (remembering that a is a digit). Thus we obtain another three answers: 1125, 4125 and 7125.

   Putting everything together, we deduce that there are six possible values of N: 1125, 3120, 4125, 6120, 7125 and 9120.

   CHECK   It is easy to check that each of these six integers is an exact multiple of 15, and clearly the middle two digits of each of them are '12' in that order.

   > We have only checked that each of our six numbers works; what we cannot check is that we have not missed one.

2. Consider the two-digit integers with one digit 3 and one digit 4. Such an integer is not divisible by 3 because the sum of the digits is $3 + 4 = 7$, which is not divisible by 3, where we use the fact that *an*

integer is divisible by 3 when the sum of the digits is divisible by 3, and not otherwise. It follows that the required integer cannot have just two digits, and so contains at least three digits.

We continue to consider divisibility by three, always using the fact that *an integer is divisible by 3 when the sum of the digits is divisible by 3, and not otherwise.*

Fac
15.3
p 8

A three-digit integer of the required form would have digits 3, 3, 4 or 3, 4, 4 in some order. The corresponding sum of digits would be $3 + 3 + 4 = 10$ or $3 + 4 + 4 = 11$, neither of which is divisible by 3. We deduce that the required integer cannot have three digits, and therefore contains at least four digits.

A four-digit integer would have digits 3, 3, 3, 4 or 3, 3, 4, 4 or 3, 4, 4, 4 in some order. Only in the case 3, 4, 4, 4 is the sum of the digits divisible by 3—in that case the sum of the digits is 12, whereas in the other cases it is 11 or 13. The list of all integers with digits 3, 4, 4, 4 in some order is 3444, 4344, 4434 and 4443.

> Here we have ordered the list by considering the position of the digit 3, which also happens to put the numbers in numerical order. The important thing is that we have been systematic, so that we can be sure that every possible number is included in the list.

Now the required integer is also divisible by 4, so the integer formed by the last two digits will be divisible by 4, from the fact that *an integer is divisible by 4 when the integer formed by the last two digits is divisible by 4, and not otherwise.* Of the integers in our list, only 3444 and 4344 meet this condition, since 44 is a multiple of 4, whereas 34 and 43 are not. And the smallest of these is 3444, which is therefore the answer to the problem.

Fa
15.
p

CHECK   The only digits in 3444 are 3 and 4, each of which occurs at least once; also $3444 \div 3 = 1128$ and $3444 \div 4 = 861$, so that 3444 is divisible by both 3 and 4.

> We have only checked that 3444 has the required properties; what we cannot check is that 3444 is the smallest such number.

3. Let the integer that Anastasia thinks of be a.

> We introduce a letter to represent the unkown that we are asked about.

Then Barry's integer is $2a$, Charlie's is $6a$ and Damion's is $36a$.

The sum of these four integers is $a + 2a + 6a + 36a$, which is $45a$.

Eve notices that this number is a perfect square, so $45a$ is a square integer. We also know that $45a$ is positive since a is positive.

Now $45 = 3 \times 3 \times 5$. So, using *the prime factors of a square occur in pairs*, we deduce that the least value of a which makes $45a$ a positive square integer is 5. And then $45a = 3 \times 3 \times 5 \times 5$.

Therefore the smallest integer that Anastasia could have thought of is 5.

CHECK When $a = 5$, Eve finds the sum of the four numbers 5, 10, 30 and 180. The sum of these is 225, which is a perfect square, so that $a = 5$ does indeed satisfy the conditions of the question.

> This does not check, of course, that 5 is the *smallest* such value. To do that, we would need to show that none of 1, 2, 3, and 4 works.

4. Now $15 = 3 \times 5$, so that an integer is divisible by 15 when it is divisible both by 3 and by 5, and not otherwise, using the fact that *an integer is divisible by pq, where p and q are prime, when it is both divisible by p and divisible by q, and not otherwise.*

Using the idea discussed in "Consecutive integers" on page 100, we let the five consecutive integers be $(n - 2)$, $(n - 1)$, n, $(n + 1)$ and $(n + 2)$ where n is at least 2. The sum of these integers is $5n$, which is always divisible by 5, whatever the value of n is.

Now $5n$ is divisible by 3 when n is divisible by 3, and not otherwise (because 5 is not divisible by 3). So five consecutive integers have a sum divisible by 3 when the middle integer is divisible by 3, and not otherwise.

Therefore five consecutive integers have a sum divisible by 15 when the middle integer is divisible by 3, and not otherwise.

CHECK Let the middle integer be $3m$ for some integer m. Then the five integers are $3m - 2$, $3m - 1$, $3m$, $3m + 1$ and $3m + 2$, which have sum $(3m - 2) + (3m - 1) + 3m + (3m + 1) + (3m + 2) = 15m$ as required.

> The check only shows that all the integers of the form $3m$ work; it does not show that none of the other integers work. Though it is possible to check this, it is not really sensible to do so—it is better to check the algebra in our solution!

5. (a) Consider the three consecutive integers $n - 1$, n and $n + 1$ (using the idea discussed in "Consecutive integers" on page 100). The sum of these integers is $3n$ and is therefore a multiple of three, whatever the value of the integer n.

   (b) Consider the four consecutive integers $n - 1$, n, $n + 1$ and $n + 2$. For all values of n, the sum of these four integers is $4n + 2$, which is never a multiple of 4, whatever the value of the integer n. So it is not true that the sum of four consecutive integers is always divisible by four—it never is!

   > Another way to prove that a statement is false is to find a *counterexample*. In this case we need to find a particular value for n for which the statement is not true. But we know from above that the statement is *never* true, hence any value of n will do. So pick, say, $n = 34$; then the sum of the four consecutive integers is $33 + 34 + 35 + 36 = 138$, which is not divisible by 4. Therefore the statement is false when n is 34.

   So the statement "the sum of four consecutive integers is always a multiple of four" is incorrect.

   (c) We deal with the odd and even cases separately.

   > We may suspect what is going on from the examples above, where k is 3 and 4, and from any other examples we try. It looks as if the statement is true when k is odd, but false when k is even. However, we will not be able to prove this general result by considering examples, we need to give a reasoned argument.

   k odd

   Suppose that the number of consecutive integers is odd. In other words, suppose that k is odd.

Let the middle integer be n, and consider the pair of integers on either side of n. They are $n - 1$ and $n + 1$, and these two integers add up to $2n$.

Consider the pair of integers on either side of these three. They are $n - 2$ and $n + 2$, and once again these two integers add up to $2n$. Because there is an odd number of integers, we may keep pairing them in this way (apart from the middle one, of course).

On each occasion, the sum of the pair is $2n$; in other words, adding the pair to the sum of all the integers increases the sum by $2n$. Which is the same as increasing the sum of all the integers by n for each integer in the list. But there are k integers in the list, so that the sum of all the integers is $k \times n$, which is always a multiple of k.

Therefore "the sum of k consecutive integers is always a multiple of k" is true whenever k is odd.

k even

Now suppose there is an even number of consecutive integers. In other words, that k is even.

Since k is even, there are two integers in the middle; let these be n and $n + 1$. The sum of these two integers is $2n + 1$, an odd number.

Now consider the pair of integers on either side of the middle two. They are $n - 1$ and $n + 2$, and these two integers add up to $2n + 1$.

Consider the pair of integers on either side of these four. They are $n - 2$ and $n + 3$, and once again these two integers add up to $2n + 1$. Because there is an even number of integers, we may keep pairing them in this way.

On each occasion, the sum of the pair is $2n + 1$; in other words, adding the pair to the sum of all the integers increases the sum by $2n + 1$. Which is the same as increasing the sum of all the integers by $\frac{1}{2}(2n + 1)$ for each integer in the list. But there are k integers in the list, so that the sum of all the integers is $k \times \frac{1}{2}(2n + 1)$.

Let the sum of all the integers be S. Then

$$S \div k = \tfrac{1}{2}(2n + 1),$$

which is not an integer since $2n + 1$ is an odd number. Hence S is not divisible by k.

Therefore "the sum of k consecutive integers is always a multiple of k" is *never* true when k is even.

6. No digit of N is exactly divisible by 2, so no digit can be 0, 2, 4, 6 or 8.

Also, no digit of N is exactly divisible by 3 or by 5. Therefore 3, 5 and 9 are also excluded as digits of N. This leaves only 1 and 7 as possible digits of N.

Now a three-digit integer that consist of only 1s and 7s can have zero, one, two or three 1s. We shall test each case for divisibility by 3, recalling that *an integer is divisible by 3 when the sum of the digits is divisible by 3, and not otherwise.*

Fac 15.: p 8

> We use divisibility facts to try to narrow down the number of options for the digits.

No 1s

When there are no 1s, the digit sum is $7 + 7 + 7 = 21$, which is divisible by 3. We deduce that 777 is divisible by 3 and is thus not a possible value of N.

Exactly one 1

When there is exactly one 1, the digit sum is $1 + 7 + 7 = 15$, which is divisible by 3. We deduce that no value of N is possible in this case.

Exactly two 1s

When there are exactly two 1s, the digit sum is $1 + 1 + 7 = 9$, which is divisible by 3. So there is also no possible value of N in this case.

Exactly three 1s

When there are exactly three 1s, the digit sum is $1 + 1 + 1 = 3$ and once again there is no possible value of N.

> Notice that we have been careful to search in a systematic way.

Hence there are no three-digit integers which satisfy the conditions given in the question.

7. Note that when $n = 1$ then the first fraction does not simplify by cancelling (though it does simplify).

> The question simply asks us to "Find a fraction $\dfrac{m}{n}$ ... ", so we only need one example. It turns out that there are an infinite number of fractions that fit the bill, but it seems sensible to try to find an example in which m or n is small. We know that $n = 1$ does not work, so let us try the next smallest possible value of n after 1; in other words, we try $n = 2$.

Suppose that the six fractions

$$\frac{m}{2}, \ \frac{m+1}{3}, \ \frac{m+2}{4}, \ \frac{m+3}{5}, \ \frac{m+4}{6}, \ \frac{m+5}{7}.$$

can be simplified by cancelling.

Then, from the first fraction, m is even. But in that case, each of

$$\frac{m+2}{4} \quad \text{and} \quad \frac{m+4}{6}$$

has an even numerator and an even denominator, so they too can be simplified by cancelling.

From the remaining fractions, we deduce that $m + 1$ is divisible by 3, that $m + 3$ is divisible by 5 and that $m + 5$ is divisible by 7.

Now $m + 3$ is odd, so the units digit of $m + 3$ is 5 (from the fact that *an integer is divisible by 5 when the last digit is 0 or 5, and not otherwise*). Let $m + 3$ have the form '$U5$' (in other words, U is the integer obtained by removing the units digit of $m + 3$). Then $m + 1$ has the form '$U3$' and $m + 5$ has the form '$U7$'. But '$U3$' is divisible by 3, so that U is divisible by 3; and '$U7$' is divisible by 7, so that U is divisible by 7. Therefore U is divisible by 21, using the fact that *an integer is divisible by pq, where p and q are prime, when it is both divisible by p and divisible by q, and not otherwise.*

Let us try $U = 21$.

> Remember, we are just trying to find *any* fraction that works.

Then $m + 3 = $ '$U5$', which is 215, and the fractions are

$$\frac{2}{212}, \ \frac{3}{213}, \ \frac{4}{214}, \ \frac{5}{215}, \ \frac{6}{216}, \ \frac{7}{217},$$

each of which can indeed be simplified by cancelling, as required.

The fractions can be simplified by cancelling, for example, 2, 3, 2, 5, 2 and 7 respectively.

Exercise 8

1. Let the integer beneath the 1 be a, as shown.

> We introduce a letter for an unknown. There are five choices of which box to choose, but it turns out they all lead to the same solution.

Using *the sum of the integers from 1 to n is equal to $\frac{1}{2}n(n+1)$* with $n = 7$, we find that the sum of the integers from 1 to 7 is 28.

> In this case, of course, it is possible just to add up the integers: $1 + 2 + 3 + 4 + 5 + 6 + 7 = 28$.

Thus the total of all the integers in the squares is 28, and each of the integers a and 2 occurs in one row and one column, that is, in two of the three line totals. Therefore the sum of the three line totals is $28 + a + 2 = 30 + a$.

But the three line totals are equal, so $30 + a$ is divisible by three. Because 30 is divisible by three, it follows that a is divisible by three. Thus the only possible values for a are 3 and 6. Let us consider each of these in turn.

$a = 3$

In this case, each line total is $33 \div 3 = 11$. Using this, we can complete some of the squares, as shown.

	1		
3	6	2
7		

There are two integers left, namely 4 and 5, which may be entered into the remaining empty squares in two different ways.

We have used each of the integers 1, 2, 3, 4, 5, 6 and 7 exactly once, and so there are two possible solutions when $a = 3$.

$a = 6$

In this case, each line total is $36 \div 3 = 12$. Using this, we can complete some of the squares, as shown.

1		
6	4	2
5		

There are two integers left, namely 7 and 3, which may be entered into the remaining empty squares in two different ways.

Once again, we have used each of the integers 1, 2, 3, 4, 5, 6 and 7 exactly once, and so there are two possible solutions when $a = 6$.

Therefore altogether there are four possible ways that the integers can be placed.

2. (a) The required integers lie between 1000 and 2000, so we know that the integer has four digits and that the leading digit is 1. Any such integer has the form '$1zyx$', where x, y and z are digits. If the integer is ascending, then x is greater than y, which is greater than z, which is greater than 1.

Suppose we consider a particular value of z, then how many choices are there for y and x? For a given z, each choice of y and x can be represented by placing a dot at the point (x, y) on a graph, as shown in the following examples.

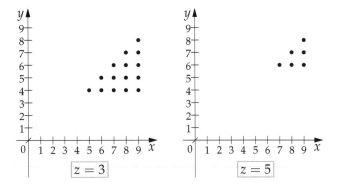

In each figure, the number of dots is a triangular number (see page 85). The values range from a maximum of 21 when $z = 2$, to a minimum of 1 when $z = 7$.

Thus the total number of ascending integers between 1000 and 2000 is $21 + 15 + 10 + 6 + 3 + 1 = 56$.

(b) Working in a similar way to (a), we find that the total number of ascending integers between 2000 and 3000 is $15 + 10 + 6 + 3 + 1$. The only difference is that we do not include the graph where $z = 2$.

Continuing in this way and putting everything together, we see that the number of ascending integers between 1000 and 10 000 is

$$56 + (15 + 10 + 6 + 3 + 1) +$$
$$(10 + 6 + 3 + 1) + (6 + 3 + 1) + (3 + 1) + 1 = 126.$$

3. Notice that any path from A to B of the specified form will cross each of the seven diagonal lines shown in the following diagram exactly once.

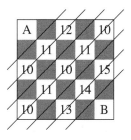

Therefore a lower bound for the sum may be obtained by adding together the smallest values along each diagonal, which gives $5 + 10 + 5 + 10 + 5 + 13 + 5 = 53$. As a consequence, a sum of 51 is definitely not possible.

Thus there are no paths giving a sum of 51.

4. Let us draw some figures, labelling the small square at which Jack finishes by the total number of steps taken.

We consider what happens if Jack only takes one step, then what happens if he takes two, and so on.

When the total number of steps is 1, we obtain figure A.

Figure A

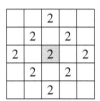

Figure B

When the total number of steps is 2, we obtain figure B, which we get by writing 2 in any square neighbouring a 1 in figure A.

Remember that, because Jack may visit a small square more than once, he is allowed to step out and back again, thus ending up on the starting square. Indeed, the best way to think of his second step is that it follows his first! So we need to write a 2 in any square neighbouring a 1 in the previous diagram.

When the total number of steps is 3, we get figure C. Once again, we write a 3 in any square neighbouring a 2 in the previous diagram.

			3			
		3		3		
	3		3		3	
3		3		3		3
	3		3		3	
		3		3		
			3			

Figure C

Finally, we write a 4 in any square neighbouring a 3 in the previous diagram, to obtain figure D.

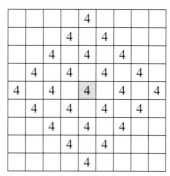

Figure D

The number 4 appears 25 times in this figure, so that Jack could finish in 25 different small squares.

5. (a) The possible numbers are 222, 223, 232, 233, 323, 323, 332 and 333.

Consider placing these above one another in order to add them, and look at the units, tens and hundreds column separately. There are four digits 2 and four digits 3 in each of these three columns. Now a digit 2 in each column adds 222 to the total, and a digit 3 in each column adds 333 to the total. Therefore the total of the numbers is $4 \times 222 + 4 \times 333$, which is $4 \times 555 = 2220$.

> We can think of this in a different way, as follows.
>
> Consider the units column. There are fours 2s and four 3s, making a total of 20. This is the same for every column and so the total is 20 from the units, 200 from the tens column, and 2000 from the hundreds column. So the overall total is $20 + 200 + 2000 = 2220$.

Therefore the require sum is 2220.

(b) When dealing with six-digit numbers, each of the digits can be either 2 or 3, that is, there are two choices. So in all there are $2 \times 2 \times 2 \times 2 \times 2 \times 2 = 2^6$ six-digit numbers of the given form.

Consider placing these numbers above one another in order to add them. Half of the units column consists of digits 2 and the other half consists of digits 3. The same is true in every column.

Since $222\,222 + 333\,333 = 555\,555$, the sum of all possible six-digit numbers of the given form is $2 \times 2 \times 2 \times 2 \times 2 \times 555\,555$, which is $32 \times 555\,555$.

> Another way to see this is as follows.
>
> Every column is made up from 32 2s and 32 3s, so the total for that column is the same as adding together 32 5s. Thus the tens column has a total of 32×50, the hundreds 32×500, and so on. Therefore the overall total is $32 \times (5 + 50 + 500 + 5000 + 50\,000 + 500\,000) = 32 \times 555\,555$.

Now $32 \times 555\,555$ is equal to $2^5 \times 3 \times 5 \times 7 \times 11 \times 13 \times 37$, because $111\,111 = 1001 \times 111$, and $1001 = 7 \times 11 \times 13$ and $111 = 3 \times 37$, as given in the example on page 90.

Exercise 9

1. Let the long side of the smaller rectangles have length p cm and the short side have length q cm.

> We need to introduce two letters since each rectangle has two unknown dimensions; we choose the smaller rectangle in order to avoid fractions.

Now each rectangle has perimeter 58 cm, and the perimeter of any rectangle is twice the sum of the lengths of the sides, so we have

$$2p + 2q = 58,$$

and so, subtracting $2p$ from each side, we obtain

$$2q = 58 - 2p. \tag{1}$$

Let the number of small rectangles be n. Then the larger rectangle has height np cm and breadth q cm. Thus the perimeter of the large rectangle, in cm, is $2np + 2q$, which equals $2np + 58 - 2p$ from equation (1).

But the perimeter of the large rectangle is 300 cm, so we have

$$2np + 58 - 2p = 300$$

and so, subtracting 58 from each side, we get

$$2np - 2p = 242.$$

Dividing each term by $2p$, we obtain

$$n - 1 = \frac{121}{p}.$$

Now p and $n - 1$ are positive integers, and so $\dfrac{121}{p}$ is also a positive integer. Therefore p is 1, 11 or 121 since these are the only factors of 121.

However, q is a positive integer. It is greater than 0, so $29 - p$ is also greater than 0, from equation (1), and therefore p is less than 29. Thus the only possibilities for p are 1 and 11. The corresponding values of n are 122 and 12.

Therefore there are exactly two possible values for the number of small rectangles.

From equation (1) the corresponding values of q are 28 and 18. Now the large rectangle has size q cm $\times$ np cm. So when $n = 122$ the size of the large rectangle is 28 cm $\times$ 122 cm, and when $n = 12$ it is 18 cm $\times$ 132 cm.

CHECK   122 small rectangles with length 28 cm and breadth 1 cm form a large rectangle with length 28 cm and breadth 122 cm and a perimeter of 300 cm; also, 12 small rectangles with length 18 cm and breadth 11 cm form a large rectangle of length 18 cm and breadth 132 cm and perimeter 300 cm. Thus in each case the given conditions are satisfied, so each of them is possible.

Our method also shows that these are the *only* values that work.

2.   (a) Let the two-digit integer be 'ab'.

The notation 'ab' means $10a + b$ in the decimal number system.

Then the integer with digits reversed is 'ba' with 'value' $10b + a$. Increasing any number by 75% is the same as multiplying by $\frac{7}{4}$ (using the method described in "Percentages" on page 94), so the information given in the question leads to the equation

$$10b + a = \tfrac{7}{4} \times (10a + b).$$

Multiplying both sides by 4, we obtain

$$40b + 4a = 7 \times (10a + b)$$

so that

$$40b + 4a = 70a + 7b.$$

Hence, subtracting $4a$ from each side, we get

$$40b = 66a + 7b$$

and now, subtracting $7b$ from each side, we obtain

$$33b = 66a.$$

Finally, dividing both sides by 33, we get

$$b = 2a.$$

Remember that a and b are digits, so that neither a nor b can be more than 9. So from the last equation the only possibilities are $a = 1, 2, 3,$ or 4. It follows that the two-digit number is 12, 24, 36 or 48.

CHECK $\frac{7}{4} \times 12 = 21$; $\frac{7}{4} \times 24 = 42$; $\frac{7}{4} \times 36 = 63$ and $\frac{7}{4} \times 48 = 84$. So these integers do indeed satisfy the conditions.

> Our method also shows that these are the *only* values that work.

(b) Let the three-digit integer be '*abc*' which means $100a + 10b + c$ in the decimal number system. Just as in part (a), we may form an equation from the given information:

$$100c + 10b + a = \tfrac{7}{4} \times (100a + 10b + c).$$

Multiplying both sides by 4, we get

$$400c + 40b + 4a = 7 \times (100a + 10b + c)$$

and so

$$400c + 40b + 4a = 700a + 70b + 7c.$$

Hence, subtracting $4a$ and $40b$ and also $7c$ from each side, we obtain

$$393c = 696a + 30b.$$

Finally, dividing every term by 3, we get

$$131c = 232a + 10b.$$

The right-hand side is even, so the left-hand side is even. But 131 is odd, so that c is even. Let $c = 2k$ for some integer k. Note that, since c is a digit (and cannot be zero), k is at most 4 (and is positive). Thus we have

$$262k = 232a + 10b$$

Dividing each term by 2, we get

$$131k = 116a + 5b.$$

We may rearrange this to give

$$130k + k = 115a + a + 5b$$

so that

$$130k + (k - a) = 115a + 5b. \tag{*}$$

Now $130k, 115a$ and $5b$ are all divisible by 5. Therefore $k - a$ is divisible by 5. Considering the ranges of values that a and k can take, together with equation (*), the only possibility is $k - a = 0$. This means that $k = a$. We have

$$130k + 0 = 115k + 5b$$

and, subtracting $115k$ from each side, we obtain

$$15k = 5b.$$

Finally, dividing by 5, we get

$$3k = b.$$

We therefore have $a = k$, $b = 3k$, $c = 2k$, and so the possible three-digit integers are 132, 264 and 396.

CHECK $\frac{7}{4} \times 132 = 231$; $\frac{7}{4} \times 264 = 462$ and $\frac{7}{4} \times 396 = 693$. So each of these integers satisfies the given conditions.

> Our method also shows that these are the *only* values that work.

3. The smallest and largest primes in the diagram are 29 and 73. The primes from 29 to 73 are

$$29, 31, 37, 41, 43, 47, 53, 59, 61, 67, 71 \text{ and } 73.$$

This list contains 12 primes, so each of these primes is used in the one of the 12 empty circles.

Thus the primes still to be placed are

$$31, 37, 43, 53, 59, 61 \text{ and } 71. \qquad (*)$$

Let two of the missing primes be a and b as shown.

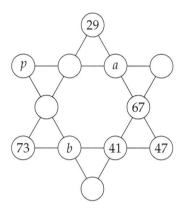

Then, from the magic hexagram property, all lines of four circles have the same total, and so

$$29 + a + 67 + 47 = 73 + b + 41 + 47$$

so that

$$a + 143 = b + 161$$

and hence, subtracting 143 from each side, we have

$$a = b + 18.$$

From the list (*), the only possibilities, using primes which differ by 18, are $a = 61$ and $b = 43$, or $a = 71$ and $b = 53$, illustrated in the following diagrams.

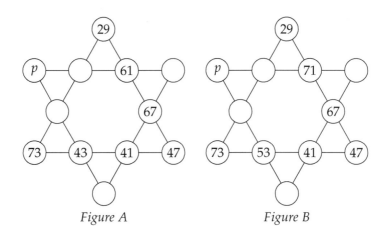

Figure A   Figure B

In figure A, the total of four circles in a line is $29 + 61 + 67 + 47 = 204$ and the primes still to be placed are

31, 37, 53, 59 and 71.

Notice that one of these primes is, indeed, p. Therefore, using the two lines containing p, we have

$$31 + 37 + 53 + 59 + 71 + 61 + 43 + p = 2 \times 204$$

so that

$$355 + p = 408.$$

Hence, subtracting 355 from each side, we have

$$p = 53.$$

> This does not show that such a magic hexagram exists, only that *if* it exists, then $p = 53$. We need to confirm (as we do below) that the other primes can be placed as required.

In figure B, the total of four circles in a line is $29 + 71 + 67 + 47 = 214$ and the primes still to be placed are

31, 37, 43, 59 and 61.

From the two lines containing p, we have

$$31 + 37 + 43 + 59 + 61 + 71 + 53 + p = 2 \times 214$$

so that

$$355 + p = 428.$$

Hence, subtracting 355 from each side, we have

$$p = 73.$$

But 73 already appears in the diagram, so this case is not possible. Hence $p = 53$ is the only possibility.

To finish the solution, we need to show that the diagram can be completed so that it has all the required properties. There is more than one way to achieve this; only one is shown.

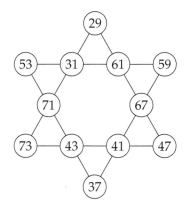

4. Let n be the number of tiles of each type.

Now a square tile of side 1 cm has an area of 1 cm^2, and a square tile of side 2 cm has an area of 4 cm^2. Therefore the total area, in cm^2, of n tiles of each type is

$$n \times 1 + n \times 4 = n + 4n$$
$$= 5n.$$

But we want to use these tiles to make a square, so that $5n$ cm^2 is equal to the area of a square, and hence $5n$ is a square. We are therefore looking for a square that is a multiple of 5.

The smallest such square is $5^2 = 25$. In that case, we have $5n = 25$, so that $n = 5$. However, the following argument—an example of a *colouring argument*—shows that it is *not* possible to use five of each type of tile to make a square.

> It is not sufficient just to say something like "no matter how I try, I cannot place five 2×2 squares on a 5×5 square", because perhaps the next time you try you will succeed! What we need to do is *prove* that it is *never* possible.

Shade four cells of a 5×5 square, as shown, and imagine placing a 2×2 square so that it covers four cells. No matter where you place the square, it will cover exactly one grey cell. But there are only four grey cells, so you can only place four 2×2 squares (without overlaps).

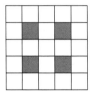

This means that it is not possible to use five tiles of each type.

After 5^2, the next largest square that is a multiple of 5 is $10^2 = 100$. In that case, we have $5n = 100$, so that $n = 20$. The next figure shows one way to make a square with 20 of each type of tile (there are many other ways). So in this case it *is* possible.

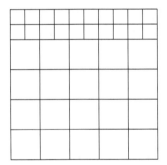

Therefore the smallest square that can be made with equal numbers of each type of tile is a 10×10 square.

5. All integers are divisible by 1, so the condition for divisibility by 1 in each part makes no restriction on the number, and thus can be ignored.

   (a) Since $1 + 2 + 3 = 6$, all six three-digit integers that can be made from the digits 1, 2 and 4 are divisible by 3, because *an integer is divisible by 3 when the sum of the digits is divisible by 3, and not otherwise.* However, b is even from the condition that 'ab' is divisible by 2, because *an integer is divisible by 2 when the last digit is even, and not otherwise.* So *a* and *c* are 1 and 3 in some order and the required integers are therefore 123 and 321.

CHECK $12 = 2 \times 6$ and $123 = 3 \times 41$; and $32 = 2 \times 16$ and $321 = 3 \times 107$. So these integers satisfy the given conditions.

> Our method also shows that these are the *only* values that work.

(b) Because '*ab*' is divisible by 2, the digit *b* is even, because *an integer is divisible by 2 when the last digit is even, and not otherwise.* Also, because '*abcd*' is divisible by 4, the digit *d* is even.

Therefore *a* and *c* are 1 and 3. But '*abc*' is divisible by 3, so that the sum of the digits is divisible by 3, because *an integer is divisible by 3 when the sum of the digits is divisible by 3, and not otherwise.* Thus *b* = 2, and therefore *d* = 4.

However, neither 14 nor 34 is divisible by 4. Since these are the only options for the last two digits, the four-digit integer cannot be divisible by 4 (using the fact that *an integer is divisible by 4 when the integer formed by the last two digits is divisible by 4, and not otherwise*).

Therefore there are no four-digit integers with the required properties.

(c) Using the given digits, the only way that '*ab cde*' can be divisible by 5 is for *e* to be 5, because *an integer is divisible by 5 when the last digit is 0 or 5, and not otherwise.* This leaves digits 1 to 4 for '*abcd*'. But from part (b), there are no four-digit integers with the necessary properties. Therefore there are no integers '*ab cde*' with the required properties.

(d) Using similar arguments, we know that *e* = 5 and that *b*, *d* and *f* are even. Therefore *a* and *c* are 1 and 3 in some order. But '*abc*' is divisible by 3, so that the sum of the digits is divisible by 3, because *an integer is divisible by 3 when the sum of the digits is divisible by 3, and not otherwise.* The only possibility is *b* = 2.

Also, '*abcd*' is divisible by 4. However, neither 14 nor 34 is divisible by 4, whereas 16 and 36 are, so *d* = 6 (we have used the fact that *an integer is divisible by 4 when the integer formed by the last two digits is divisible by 4, and not otherwise*). Thus *f* = 4 since 4 is the only unused even digit, and the integer is '*a2c 654*'.

We have not tested for divisibility by 6. But the sum of the digits 1, 2, 3, 4, 5 and 6 is 21, which is divisible by 3, so all the possible integers made from these digits are divisible by 3 (from the fact that *an integer is divisible by 3 when the sum of the digits is divisible by 3, and not otherwise*). Since '*a2c* 654' is even, it is therefore divisible by 6, using the fact that *an integer is divisible by pq, where p and q are prime, when it is both divisible by p and divisible by q, and not otherwise*.

Hence there are two six-digit integers with the required properties: 123 654 and 321 654.

CHECK $12 = 2 \times 6$, $123 = 3 \times 41$, $1236 = 4 \times 309$, $12\,365 = 5 \times 2473$, $123\,654 = 6 \times 20\,609$; and $32 = 2 \times 16$, $321 = 3 \times 107$, $3216 = 4 \times 804$, $32\,165 = 5 \times 6433$, $321\,654 = 6 \times 53\,609$. So these two integers do satisfy the given conditions.

> Our method also shows that these are the *only* values that work.

6. Remember that the prime numbers are 2, 3, 5, 7, 11, 13, 17, 19, 23, 29, 31, 37, 41, 43, ...

The sum of four odd positive integers is even and bigger than 2, so cannot be prime. Therefore the four primes cannot all be odd. But 2 is the only even prime number, so that one of the four primes is 2.

Similarly, the sum of two odd primes is even and bigger than 2, so cannot be prime. Therefore one of the pair is even, and hence 2 is one of the pair.

Also, the sum of the triple is prime, so that 2 is not one of the triple, otherwise the sum of the triple would be even and greater than 2. We conclude that the four numbers are 2 and a triple of odd primes.

Now the sum of the three smallest odd primes is $3 + 5 + 7 = 15$ so that the sum of the triple is at least 15. However, the sum of the triple is prime, and adding 2 to the sum of the triple gives the sum of all four numbers, which is also prime. Hence the possible sums of the triple are the primes 17, 29, 41, ..., with the primes 19, 31, 43, ... as the corresponding sums of all four numbers.

Fac 15.3 p 8

Fac 15.3 p 9

> We are asked to find the *smallest* sum of four primes, so our approach is essentially to work through these primes in order, starting at the smallest, and find the first value that works. We start with 19; if that fails, then we try 31; and so on.

But no triple of prime numbers has sum 17 (we have seen that $3 + 5 + 7 = 15$ and the next prime is 11, which is too big). Therefore the sum of the triple is at least 29 and the sum of the four primes is at least 31.

Moreover, a sum of 31 can actually be achieved. For example, the four primes 2, 5, 7 and 17 add up to 31. In that case, the pair could be 2 and 5, and the triple 5, 7 and 17.

So the smallest possible sum of the four prime numbers is 31.

CHECK $2 + 5 = 7, 5 + 7 + 17 = 29, 2 + 5 + 7 + 17 = 31$ and 7, 29 and 31 are all prime.

Exercise 10

1. Let p be the first number that Pippa thinks of. Then her five numbers are

$$p,$$
$$p + 1,$$
$$(p + 1) + 2 = p + 3,$$
$$(p + 3) + 3 = p + 6$$
$$\text{and} \quad (p + 6) + 4 = p + 10.$$

The sum of these five numbers is $5p + 20$.
Let Ben's first number be b. Then his numbers are

$$b,$$
$$b - 1,$$
$$(b - 1) - 2 = b - 3,$$
$$(b - 3) - 3 = b - 6$$
$$\text{and} \quad (b - 6) - 4 = b - 10.$$

The sum of these five numbers is $5b - 20$.
Since these two sums are equal, we have

$$5b - 20 = 5p + 20.$$

Hence, adding 20 to each side, we obtain

$$5b = 5p + 40.$$

Therefore, subtracting $5p$ from each side, we get

$$5b - 5p = 40$$

and finally, dividing each term by 5, we obtain

$$b - p = 8.$$

So the difference between the numbers Pippa and Ben first thought of is 8.

CHECK   When b is 8 more than p, Ben's numbers are $p + 8, p + 7, p + 5, p + 2$ and $p - 2$. Now

$$(p + 8) + (p + 7) + (p + 5) + (p + 2) + (p - 2) = 5p + 20$$

which is, indeed, Pippa's total.

> It is not possible to find the actual numbers that Pippa and Ben used.

2. Let Jill travel at a speed of u mph for a time t hours. Then, using the fact that *distance = speed × time*, we deduce that the distance up the hill is ut miles.

Let Jack travel at a speed of v mph. He arrives at the top of the hill $1\frac{1}{2}$ hours ahead of Jill, so that he travels for $t - \frac{3}{2}$ hours. Once again using *distance = speed × time*, we deduce that the distance up the hill is $v(t - \frac{3}{2})$ miles, that is, $vt - \frac{3}{2}v$ miles.

The distance is the same in both cases, so

$$vt - \tfrac{3}{2}v = ut. \qquad (*)$$

If Jill had walked 50% faster, her speed would have been $\frac{3}{2}u$, since $100\% + 50\% = 150\%$, which is $\frac{150}{100} = \frac{3}{2}$ (using the method described in "Percentages" on page 94).

If Jack had walked 50% slower, his speed would have been $\frac{1}{2}v$ because $100\% - 50\% = 50\%$, which is $\frac{50}{100} = \frac{1}{2}$ (once again using the method described in "Percentages").

However, Jack and Jill left the bottom at the same time and would have arrived at the top together, so they would have travelled at the same speed. In other words,

$$\tfrac{1}{2}v = \tfrac{3}{2}u$$

Multiplying each side by 2, we obtain

$$v = 3u.$$

But, multiplying each term in equation $(*)$ by 3, we get

$$3vt - \tfrac{9}{2}v = 3ut.$$

We have already found that $v = 3u$, so that

$$3vt - \tfrac{9}{2}v = vt.$$

Adding $\tfrac{9}{2}v$ to each side, we obtain

$$3vt = vt + \tfrac{9}{2}v$$

that is, subtracting vt from each side,

$$2vt = \tfrac{9}{2}v.$$

Dividing each side by $2v$ (which is not zero), we get

$$t = \tfrac{9}{4}.$$

> In the working above, we need to check that $2v$ is not zero, because division by zero is *never* allowed.

Thus Jill took $\tfrac{9}{4}$ hours, which is 2 hours and 15 minutes (or 135 minutes), to walk up the hill.

CHECK   To reach the top at the same time, Jill and Jack would have travelled the same distance in the same time.

Jack took three-quarters of an hour to go up the hill, if he had walked half as fast, he would have taken twice as long, so Jack would have taken one and a half hours.

Jill took two and a quarter hours to go up the hill. Had she walked one and a half times as fast, she would have taken two thirds as long, that is, one and a half hours to go up the hill since $\tfrac{2}{3} \times 135$ minutes $=$ 2×45 minutes $= 90$ minutes which is, indeed, the same time as that taken by Jack.

3. Let the amount that Amy received be $60k$ pence.

> Since we want to divide the amount that Amy received by 2, 3, 4 and 5, it seems sensible to let that amount be $60k$ pence because 60 is exactly divisible by each of 2, 3, 4 and 5.

Then, in turn, her brothers received 30k pence, 20k pence, 15k pence and 12k pence.

Now each child received a whole number of pence, so each of 60k, 30k, 20k, 15k and 12k should be an integer.

We do not know which of the four brothers Peter and Tom are. All we know is that Peter received 30 pence less than Tom, so that Tom received more than Peter. The possible numbers of pence that Tom and Peter could have received are shown in the table.

Tom	Peter
30k	20k
30k	15k
30k	12k
20k	15k
20k	12k
15k	12k

> We ensure that no cases are missed by listing all possibilities in a systematic way. We have used a decreasing order here: for each amount that Tom may have, we list all the possibilities for the amount that Peter may have.

Let us consider in turn each of the possible numbers of pence that Tom and Peter could have received, and see what happens when the difference between them is 30.

30k and 20k

In this case 30k − 20k = 30 and therefore 10k = 30, so that k = 3. Hence the number of pence that Amy received was $60 \times 3 = 180$.

30k and 15k

In this case 30k − 15k = 15k = 30, so that k = 2. Hence the number of pence that Amy received was $60 \times 2 = 120$.

30k and 12k

In this case 18k = 30, so that 60k is not an integer.

20k and 15k

In this case 5k = 30, so that k = 6. Hence the number of pence that Amy received was $60 \times 6 = 360$.

20k and 12k
  In this case $8k = 30$, so that $60k$ is not an integer.

15k and 12k
  In this case $3k = 30$, so that $k = 10$. Hence the number of pence that Amy received was $60 \times 10 = 600$.

There are therefore four possibilities for k, each of which is an integer, so that $60k$, $30k$, $20k$, $15k$ and $12k$ are integers as required.

Hence Amy received £1.20, £1.80, £3.60 or £6.

CHECK   For each of these four possibilities, we can show that all the children received a whole number of pence:

$$120 = 2 \times 60 \text{ or } 3 \times 40 \text{ or } 4 \times 30 \text{ or } 5 \times 24;$$
$$180 = 2 \times 90 \text{ or } 3 \times 60 \text{ or } 4 \times 45 \text{ or } 5 \times 36;$$
$$360 = 2 \times 180 \text{ or } 3 \times 120 \text{ or } 4 \times 90 \text{ or } 5 \times 72;$$
$$600 = 2 \times 300 \text{ or } 3 \times 200 \text{ or } 4 \times 150 \text{ or } 5 \times 120.$$

Our method also shows that these are the *only* values that work.

4. Let the distance between A and B be $4x$ miles and the distance between B and C be $4y$ miles.

Since the distance from A to B and from B to C are split into quarters, it seems sensible to use $4x$ and $4y$ for the unknowns and thereby avoid fractions. Note that we have set things up so that x and y are *numbers*.

After the friend's first reply, Calum has travelled x miles from A towards B and still has to travel $3x$ miles to reach B.

After the friend's second reply, Calum has travelled $3y$ miles from B and still has y miles to travel to reach C.

Therefore, between the two replies, Calum has travelled $3x + 3y$ miles out of a total journey of $4x + 4y$ miles.

But the distance between the two replies is ten miles. Therefore

$$3x + 3y = 10$$

Dividing by 3, we get

$$x + y = \frac{10}{3}$$

Multiplying by 4, we obtain

$$4x + 4y = \frac{40}{3}$$

$$= 13\frac{1}{3}.$$

Thus Calum will have cycled $13\frac{1}{3}$ miles from A when he reaches C.

> We do not know the position of B, nor can we work it out—this is what makes the question interesting. Thus it is not really possible to check our result, other than to note that $13\frac{1}{3} - 10 = 3\frac{1}{3}$ and $10 : 3\frac{1}{3} = 3 : 1$, so that the distance between the replies and the rest of the total distance are in the expected ratio.

5. Using the fact that *the sum of the integers from 1 to n is equal to* $\frac{1}{2}n(n + 1)$, the sum of the integers from 1 to 12 is $\frac{1}{2} \times 12 \times 13 = 78$.

Let the integer in the empty corner be s and let the total of each line of integers be T.

By considering the total of all four lines, we obtain

$$4T = 78 + \text{ the sum of the integers in the four corners}$$
$$= 78 + 5 + 12 + 6 + s$$

so that

$$4T = 101 + s. \tag{*}$$

The left-hand-side of this equation is divisible by 4, so the right-hand side is also divisible by 4. Remembering that s is a positive integer less than 12, the only possibilities for s are 3, 7 and 11. However, 3 already appears in the diagram, so the empty corner contains 7 or 11. From equation (*), this means that $4T$ is 108 or 112 and T is 27 or 28. These two cases are illustrated in the following figures.

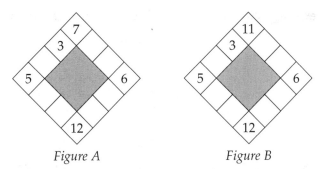

Figure A   Figure B

In figure A, the line containing 5, 3 and 7 also contains 12, in order for the line total to be 27. But 12 has already been placed, so this case is impossible.

In figure B, the line containing 5, 3 and 11 also contains 9, in order for the line total to be 28.

The integers remaining are 1, 2, 4, 7, 8 and 10.

Two more integers with a total of 10 need to be placed in the line containing 6 and 12, in order to make the line total 28. The only possible integers from those remaining are 2 and 8. There are two ways of placing this pair of numbers in the diagram, because they may be placed in either order.

Each of the remaining incomplete lines requires a total of 11 for the two empty squares. There are two pairs of the integers now remaining that total 11, namely $4 + 7$ and $10 + 1$. Either pair can be placed in one of the incomplete lines, and, once again, each of the two pairs can be placed in two different ways. So there are $2 \times 2 \times 2 = 8$ ways of placing these two pairs.

Each of these 8 ways can be used with either placement of the pair 2 and 8. So altogether there are $8 \times 2 = 16$ possible ways of completing the diagram.

> It is much better to count the possible ways of completing the diagram rather than trying to find every single possiblity by placing integers in boxes. We require certainty, and logic rather than trial and error provides this.

6. The sum of the integers from 1 to 7 is $\frac{1}{2} \times 7 \times 8 = 28$, using the fact that *the sum of the integers from 1 to n is equal to $\frac{1}{2}n(n + 1)$*.

Let the missing integers be a, b, c, d, e and f, as shown.

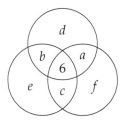

Then $a + b + c + d + e + f + 6 = 28$, so that, subtracting 6 from each side, we obtain $a + b + c + d + e + f = 22$. Also, finding the totals of the numbers in each circle, we get

$$T = a + b + d + 6,$$
$$T = b + c + e + 6$$
$$\text{and} \quad T = c + a + f + 6.$$

Adding these three equations, we obtain

$$3T = 2a + 2b + 2c + d + e + f + 18,$$

which may be written

$$3T = a + b + c + (a + b + c + d + e + f) + 18.$$

Therefore

$$3T = a + b + c + 22 + 18$$
$$= a + b + c + 40. \tag{*}$$

But $a + b + c$ is at least $1 + 2 + 3 = 6$ and at most $4 + 5 + 7 = 16$. Therefore $3T$ is at least 46 and at most 56. The multiples of 3 between 46 and 56 are 48, 51 and 54. Therefore, the only possible values for T are 16, 17 and 18.

The values $T = 16$ and $T = 18$ are possible, as shown in the following figures.

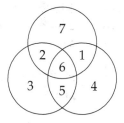
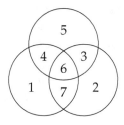

However, when $T = 17$ we have $3T = 3 \times 17$, which is 51, so that equation (*) becomes

$$51 = a + b + c + 40,$$

that is, subtracting 40 from each side,

$$11 = a + b + c.$$

Considering the total of the numbers in the 'upper' circle, we get $17 = a + b + d + 6$, that is, subtracting 6 from each side, $11 = a + b + d$. But $a + b + c$ and $a + b + d$ cannot both be equal to 11 because c and d are different. Therefore $T = 17$ is not possible.

Hence the only values of T that are possible are 16 and 18.

7. Let the first term be a and let the second term be b, where a and b are positive integers and b is greater than a.

The sequence is therefore $a, b, a + b, a + 2b, 2a + 3b, 3a + 5b, 5a + 8b, 8a + 13b, 13a + 21b$, and so on.

The eighth term is 390, so

$$8a + 13b = 390$$

and, subtracting $13b$ from each side, we obtain

$$8a = 390 - 13b. \tag{*}$$

The right-hand side of this equation is divisible by 13. This means that $8a$ is a multiple of 13. But 8 and 13 do not have a common factor greater than 1 and a is an integer, so it follows that a is a multiple of 13, that is, $a = 13k$ for some positive integer k.

Then, dividing equation (*) by 13, we get

$$8k = 30 - b.$$

Adding b to each side, we obtain

$$b + 8k = 30$$

and then, subtracting $8k$ from each side, we get

$$b = 30 - 8k.$$

But b is larger than a, so $30 - 8k$ is larger than $13k$ and therefore 30 is larger than $13k + 8k$, which equals $21k$. The only possibility is thus $k = 1$.

Hence we have $a = 13$ and $b = 22$. Thus the ninth term, which is $13a + 21b$, is equal to $13 \times 13 + 21 \times 22 = 631$.

CHECK   The sequence is 13, 22, 35, 57, 92, 149, 241, 390, 631, ..., which satisfies the conditions of the question.

8. We claim that the smallest possible number is 35. To justify this claim, we need to do two things:
   (i) show that the situation is possible with 35 sweets;
   (ii) show that the situation is not possible with a smaller number of sweets.

   Let us deal with each of these in turn.

   (i) Suppose the jars contain 5, 6, 7, 8 and 9 sweets. Then there are 35 sweets altogether. Also, no two jars contain the same number of sweets. In addition, the three jars with fewest sweets contain $5 + 6 + 7 = 18$ sweets, and the two jars with most sweets contain $8 + 9 = 17$ sweets. It follows that any three jars contain at least 18 sweets, whereas the total of the remaining two jars is at most 17. Therefore any three jars contain more sweets than the total of the remaining two jars.

   Hence it is possible to have exactly 35 sweets in the jars.

   (ii) Let the number of sweets in the five jars be a, b, c, d and e, where $a < b < c < d < e$.

   > The symbol $<$ means 'is less than'. Thus $4 < 8$ is a true statement and $4 < 2$ is not true.
   >
   > So the line above means that a, b, c, d and e are in increasing order with a being the smallest and e the largest.

   Suppose the number of sweets in the jars is less than 35, so that $a + b + c + d + e < 35$.

   Remembering that a, b, c, d and e are different integers, we know that b is at least $a + 1$, c is at least $a + 2$, d is at least $a + 3$ and e is at least $a + 4$. Therefore

   $$a + (a + 1) + (a + 2) + (a + 3) + (a + 4) < 35$$

so that

$$5a + 10 < 35$$

and hence, subtracting 10 from each side, we have

$$5a < 25.$$

Dividing both sides by 5, we get

$$a < 5.$$

Because a is a positive integer, this means that a is 1, 2, 3 or 4. Also, any three jars contain more sweets than the total of the remaining two jars, so that

$$d + e < a + b + c.$$

But d is at least $b + 2$ and e is at least $c + 2$. Therefore

$$(b + 2) + (c + 2) < a + b + c.$$

Hence, subtracting $b + c$ from each side, we get

$$4 < a.$$

Therefore a is greater than 4. But we showed above that the only possible values for a are 1, 2, 3 and 4. Hence it is impossible to find a value of a, and it follows that the situation is not possible when the number of sweets is less than 35.

9. Consider the six totals: three row totals and three column totals. For Pat to have six different totals, the smallest possible values that the totals can be are 0, 1, 2, 3, 4 and 5. And $0 + 1 + 2 + 3 + 4 + 5 = 15$.

Let T be the total number of counters that Pat uses. Then the sum of the three row totals is equal to T, and the sum of the three column totals is also equal to T.

We conclude that $2T$ is at least 15.

But T is a positive integer, so that $2T$ is a positive even integer. Hence $2T$ is at least 16, so that T is at least 8. In other words, the smallest number of counters that Pat could possibly use is 8.

We now need to see whether it is possible to achieve a solution with 8 counters. The following figure shows one way (the numbers indicate how many counters are placed in each cell).

	1	3
	1	2
		1

> In fact, there are many ways to place 8 counters so that the six row and column totals are all different.

10. Since each digit is different, none of the digits is 0.

    Notice that once we know a, b and c then all the other digits are determined.

    Also, c and $d = a + b$ are different; as are a and $e = b + c$. Thus we have $c \neq a + b$.

    > The symbol $\neq$ means 'is not equal to', or 'does not equal'.

    Therefore $c - a \neq b$. Similarly $a \neq b + c$, therefore $a - c \neq b$. As a result, we know that

    > the (positive) difference between a and c is not equal to b.   (*)

    Now

    $$
    \begin{aligned}
    f &= d + e \\
      &= (a + b) + (b + c) \\
      &= a + 2b + c
    \end{aligned}
    $$

    and f is at most 9, which means that b is at most 3.

    > Remember, we know that no digit is 0, so a and c are at least 1.

    Let us consider the different possible values of b in turn.

    > In order to be confident we have covered everything, we work systematically and consider the possible values of b in ascending order.

    $b = 1$

    We have $f = a + 2 + c$, which is at most 9. Therefore $a + c$ is at most 7. But $a + c$ cannot be 3 or 4, because the digit 1 has already been used for b. Hence $a + c$ is equal to 5, 6 or 7.

However, $a + c = 5$ is not possible, because $2 + 3$ is excluded by (*).

If $a + c = 6$, then $a = 2$ and $c = 4$, or *vice versa*.

If $a + c = 7$, then $a = 2$ and $c = 5$, or *vice versa* (note that (*) excludes $3 + 4$).

So when $b = 1$ there are four possibilities for (a, b, c, d, e, f):

$$(2, 1, 4, 3, 5, 8) \quad \text{and} \quad (4, 1, 2, 5, 3, 8);$$
$$(2, 1, 5, 3, 6, 9) \quad \text{and} \quad (5, 1, 2, 6, 3, 9).$$

$b = 2$

We have $f = a + 4 + c$, which is at most 9. Therefore $a + c$ is at most 5. But $a + c$ cannot be 3, because the digit 2 has already been used for b. So we have $a + c = 4$ or $a + c = 5$.

However, $a + c = 4$ is excluded by (*).

If $a + c = 5$, then $a = 1$ and $c = 4$, or *vice versa*.

So when $b = 2$ there are two possibilities for (a, b, c, d, e, f):

$$(1, 2, 4, 3, 6, 9) \quad \text{and} \quad (4, 2, 1, 6, 3, 9).$$

$b = 3$

We have $a + c = 3$, so that $a = 1$ and $c = 2$, or *vice versa*.

So when $b = 3$ there are two possibilities for (a, b, c, d, e, f):

$$(1, 3, 2, 4, 5, 9) \quad \text{and} \quad (2, 3, 1, 5, 4, 9).$$

Putting everything together, there are eight solutions, given in the following table.

a	b	c	d	e	f
2	1	4	3	5	8
4	1	2	5	3	8
2	1	5	3	6	9
5	1	2	6	3	9
1	2	4	3	6	9
4	2	1	6	3	9
1	3	2	4	5	9
2	3	1	5	4	9

Exercise 11

1. The volume of a rectangular block (cuboid) measuring $3\,\text{cm} \times 2\,\text{cm} \times 1\,\text{cm}$ is

$$\text{length} \times \text{breadth} \times \text{height} = 3 \times 2 \times 1\,\text{cm}^3$$
$$= 6\,\text{cm}^3.$$

Thus the total volume of all ten cuboids is $60\,\text{cm}^3$.

Now the smallest possible cube greater than 60 is $4^3 = 64$, so the box measures at least $4\,\text{cm} \times 4\,\text{cm} \times 4\,\text{cm}$.

> We have found the minimum size of cube, but we need to see whether this minimum is *attainable*, in other words, is there a way to fit the ten blocks into a $4\,\text{cm} \times 4\,\text{cm} \times 4\,\text{cm}$ cubical box?

There is more than one way to fit the cuboids in a box that is a cube with sides of length $4\,\text{cm}$. For example, we may stack eight of the cuboids, as shown in figure 1, to form a $3 \times 4 \times 4$ block.

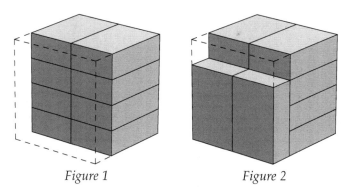

| Figure 1 | Figure 2 |

This leaves room to place two more cuboids, as shown in figure 2.

Thus the ten blocks will fit into a $4\,\text{cm} \times 4\,\text{cm} \times 4\,\text{cm}$ box, and we showed above that a box at least this big is required. Therefore the smallest box into which Tamsin could fit ten blocks measures $4\,\text{cm} \times 4\,\text{cm} \times 4\,\text{cm}$.

2. (a) Let there be w wins and d draws.

> We introduce letters for unknowns and try to set up
> some equations. We are asked for the number of draws,
> so using one letter for that is sensible. We could get away
> with just one letter, but the algebra is a little simpler with
> two.

There were 10 games altogether (one team played 4 others, the
next team had 3 others left to play, the next had 2 others to play
and the next had only 1 other to play). Each game was either a
draw, or a win for one or other side. Thus $w + d = 10$.

The total number of points resulting from the wins is $3w$, and
total number of points resulting from the draws is $2d$, because
for each draw, each of the two teams score one point. But the
total number of points was $10 + 9 + 4 + 3 + 1 = 27$. Therefore
we have

$$3w + 2d = 27,$$

which we can write as

$$w + (w + d) + (w + d) = 27.$$

Therefore

$$w + 10 + 10 = 27$$

so that, subtracting 20 from each side, we have

$$w = 7.$$

Hence $d = 10 - 7$ and therefore there were 3 draws.

CHECK   Since $7 \times 3 + 3 \times 2 = 21 + 6$, which is 27, the required
conditions are met.

> Our method also shows that these are the *only* values
> that work.

(b) Each team played 4 games.

Pinks scored 1 point, which can only have been from a draw.
Thus Pinks drew 1 game and lost 3 games.

Yellows scored 10 points from 4 games. The only way this could
happen is if Yellows won 3 games and drew 1 game.

Reds scored 9 points from 4 games. The only way this could happen is if Reds won 3 games and lost 1 game.

Greens scored 4 points from 4 games. But the match between Greens and Reds was not a draw (Reds did not draw any games). Therefore Greens did not draw 4 games, so the only way they could have scored 4 points is if they won 1 game, drew 1 game and lost 2 games.

So far we know that three teams drew a game, and one team drew no games. Therefore the final team, Blues, drew at least one game. But they scored 3 points, and therefore they drew 3 games, and lost 1 game.

All this information is included in the following table. Note that each row adds up to 4, corresponding to each team playing 4 games.

Team	Won	Drawn	Lost
Yellows	3	1	0
Reds	3	0	1
Greens	1	1	2
Blues	0	3	1
Pinks	0	1	3

Now the 3 draws of Blues can only have been against Yellows, Greens and Pinks. Therefore Blues lost against Reds, and Pinks lost against Yellows, Reds and Greens.

Thus the results in the Greens' matches were: a loss against Yellows; a loss against Reds; a draw with Blues; and a win against Pinks.

CHECK

We can check that our results agree with all the information in the question.

3. Will does not sit next to a girl and so he has a boy on either side. But there are only two other boys and so Will sits between Vince and Zac.

Vince sits beside Yvonne, and we have just found that he has Will on the other side. Therefore the order of the children round the table, either clockwise or anticlockwise, is

Zac, Will, Vince, Yvonne and Xenia,

because Xenia takes up the last place available.

But Vince sits between Yvonne and the child from Durham, so Will is from Durham.

The child from Aberdeen sits between Zac and the child from Edinburgh. But Will sits on one side of Zac, and Will is from Durham. So Xenia, on the other side of Zac, is from Aberdeen, and Yvonne, the next child, is from Edinburgh.

Zac writes to the child from Cardiff and the only child (apart from Zac himself) not yet allocated to a city is Vince. So Vince comes from Cardiff.

Finally, the only city left unallocated is Belfast. So Zac is from Belfast. The following table shows the city that each child comes from.

Child	City
Vince	Cardiff
Will	Durham
Xenia	Aberdeen
Yvonne	Edinburgh
Zac	Belfast

The following figure shows one way that the children may be seated round the table.

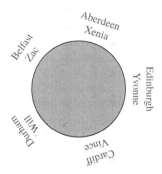

Note that we may choose whether we work clockwise or anticlockwise—it is only the relative position of the children that matters.

All the other possible seating arrangements may be obtained from this one by rotation or reflection.

4. Let us define the *predecessor* of an integer in a chain to be the integer which appears before it in the chain. In the question, 97 is the predecessor of 63.

Firstly, we note that no integer which has a prime factor p greater than 9 can have a predecessor, because p cannot be a digit since, by definition, a digit can only have an integer value from 0 to 9. For example, 22 has 11 as a prime factor and would have been obtained from 2×11 rather than as the product of two digits, so can have no predecessor.

Secondly, we note that no chain starting with a two-digit positive integer can include integers with more than two digits, because, for any two-digit integer, the greatest possible product of the digits is $9 \times 9 = 81$, which still has only two digits.

Thirdly, the last calculation also tells us that no two-digit integer greater than 81 can have a predecessor.

We are told that the required chain ends in 6. There are four ways of writing 6 as the product of two digits:

$$6 = 1 \times 6$$
$$= 2 \times 3$$
$$= 3 \times 2$$
$$= 6 \times 1.$$

Therefore there are four possible two-digit predecessors of 6, namely 16, 23, 32 and 61.

Since each of 23 and 61 has a prime factor greater than 9 (the integer itself) neither of them can have a predecessor.

Since

$$16 = 2 \times 8$$
$$= 4 \times 4$$
$$= 8 \times 2$$

and

$$32 = 4 \times 8$$
$$= 8 \times 4,$$

the possible two-digit predecessors of 16 are 28, 44 and 82, and the possible two-digit predecessors of 32 are 48 and 84. Of these, 44 can have no predecessor (because 11 is a factor), and neither of 82 or 84 can (because they are greater than 81). So we only need to consider 28 and 48.

Since

$$28 = 4 \times 7$$
$$= 7 \times 4$$

and

$$48 = 6 \times 8$$
$$= 8 \times 6$$

the possible two-digit predecessors of 28 are 47 and 74, and the possible two-digit predecessors of 48 are 68 and 86. None of these can have a predecessor (86 is too large, and the others have a prime factor that is too large). Therefore the chain is complete.

The possible two-digit first integers for a chain whose final integer is 6 are therefore 16, 23, 28, 32, 44, 47, 48, 61, 68, 74, 82, 84 and 86. The possible chains are illustrated in the following figure.

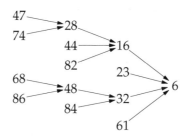

5. The total number of points scored by the three competitors was $18 + 9 + 8 = 35$.

There was more than one event and all the events had the same total score, which was greater than one. But the only ways to factorise 35, with both factors being larger than one, are 5×7 and 7×5. Therefore there were seven events each with a total score of 5 or five events each with a total score of 7.

However, each position had a different score, so the least possible total for each event was $1 + 2 + 3 = 6$, so that a total score of 5 is not possible. Therefore there were five events each with a score of 7. But $1 + 2 + 4$ is the only way to express 7 as the sum of three different positive integers, so the scores were 4 for first place, 2 for second place, and 1 for third.

Now the March Hare scored 4 points for the Sack Race, and he obtained 8 points in total. Hence the March Hare scored 4 points in total for the other four events, so he lost each of them, scoring 1 point for each.

Consider Alice's score of 18. The only way to achieve a sum of 18 with five numbers (each of which is 1, 2 or 4) is $4 + 4 + 4 + 4 + 2$. Hence Alice won four events and came second in the Sack Race.

The only unallocated position in the Sack Race is last. Therefore the Mock Turtle came last in the Sack Race, with a score of 1 point. Also, the Mock Turtle came second in each of the other events since these are the only positions remaining. Notice that $9 = 1 + 2 + 2 + 2 + 2$, as required.

The results table below shows the final scores.

Competitor	Sack Race	Every other event	Total score
Alice	2	4	18
Mock Turtle	1	2	9
March Hare	4	1	8

The March Hare was last in every event apart from the Sack Race, and so was last in the Egg and Spoon Race.

CHECK

We can check that our results agree with all the information in the question.

6. The nodes are numbered from 1 to 6, so the possible sums of two nodes are as follows.

$$3 = 1 + 2$$
$$4 = 1 + 3$$
$$5 = 1 + 4$$
$$= 2 + 3$$
$$6 = 1 + 5$$
$$= 2 + 4$$
$$7 = 1 + 6$$
$$= 2 + 5$$
$$= 3 + 4$$
$$8 = 2 + 6$$
$$= 3 + 5$$
$$9 = 3 + 6$$
$$= 4 + 5$$
$$10 = 4 + 6$$
$$11 = 5 + 6$$

Now each given network has nine edges and therefore nine different sums, so that each sum from 3 to 11 will occur, in order to satisfy the conditions given in the question.

Notice that there is only one way of obtaining a sum of 10 or 11, so that 6 will be joined to 5 and also to 4. Similarly, 1 will be joined to 2 and to 3.

(a) There are many ways to number the nodes of network A. Two possible ways are shown in the following diagrams.

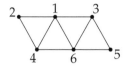 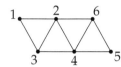

(b) We know that 6 is joined to 5 and also to 4. We also know that 1 is joined to 2 and also to 3.

But what about the pairs 4 and 5, and 2 and 3: are they joined, or not? If one pair is joined, then the corresponding group of three numbers form a small triangle, because each is connected to the others (see figure 1). If a pair is not joined, the corresponding group of three numbers form a 'line of three', with the middle one connected to those on either side, which are not themselves joined (see figure 2).

Figure 2

Figure 1

In network B, we see that there is no place for two such small triangles, nor is there a place for two such 'lines of three'. In other words, one pair is joined, and the other pair is not.

Let us suppose that 4 and 5 are joined, and that 2 and 3 are not (essentially the same argument as the following can be used when this happens the other way round—just replace nodes numbered 1, 2, 3, 4, 5, 6 by nodes numbered 6, 5, 4, 3, 2, 1).

The group 4, 5, 6 therefore forms a small triangle and the group 1, 2, 3 forms a 'line of three', with 1 in the middle. Hence we have one of the networks shown in figure C on the next page, figure D or figure E (or a rotation or reflection of one of these), where the remaining two nodes are numbered 2 and 3 (either way round).

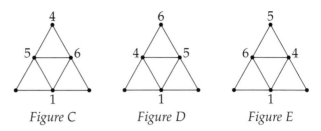

Figure C   Figure D   Figure E

Numbering the remaining nodes in figure C, we get either figure F or figure G. But in figure F the sum 7 is repeated, and in figure G the sum 8 is repeated.

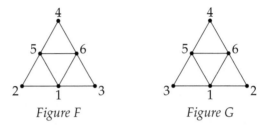

Figure F   Figure G

Similarly, numbering the remaining nodes in figure D, we obtain either figure H or figure I. But in figure H the sum 6 is repeated, and in figure I the sum 7 is repeated.

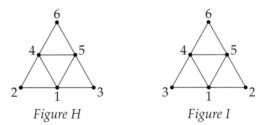

Figure H   Figure I

Finally, numbering the remaining nodes in figure E, we get either figure J or figure K. But in figure J the sum 7 is repeated, and in figure K the sum 9 is repeated.

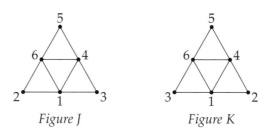

Figure J   *Figure K*

So in every case we get a repeated sum. Hence it is impossible to number network B in the required manner.

7. Consider the two-digit integer '*ab*'. There are three cases to consider.

    $b = 0$

    The value Jack obtains for any such two-digit integer is just the tens digit. But the possible tens digits are the integers from 1 to 9 . So in this case the sum of the values Jack obtains is 45.

    $b = a$

    For any two-digit integer of this form (there are 9 of them), the difference between the units and the tens digit is zero. So in this case the sum of the values Jack obtains is zero.

    $b \neq a$ and $b \neq 0$

    There are $9 \times 8 = 72$ possible two-digit integers of this form. They can be placed in pairs: *ab* pairs with *ba*. The sum of the values Jack obtains for each pair is $(a - b) + (b - a) = 0$. So in this case the sum of the values Jack obtains is also zero.

    Altogether, the sum of the values Jack obtains from all possible positive two-digit integers is 45.

8. Call the first player A and the second player B.

    When just one sweet is left on the table there is no valid move.

    We claim that A can force B to lose by leaving 15, 7, 3 and 1 sweets after successive turns. We can justify this claim as follows.

    On her first turn, A should leave 15 sweets. Then B has to leave between 8 and 14 sweets (inclusive).

    No matter how many sweets are now on the table, A should leave 7 on her next turn. This will always be possible because 7 is at least half of the number of sweets remaining. Next, player B has to leave between 4 and 6 sweets.

Player A can then leave 3 sweets because 3 is at least half of the number of sweets remaining. Player B now has to take 1 sweet, leaving 2 on the table.

Finally, A takes 1 sweet, leaving 1 sweet on the table. As a result, B has no valid move and A wins.

Exercise 12

1.

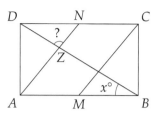

Since $ABCD$ is a rectangle, $CD = AB = 2$ and $\angle NDA$ is a right angle.

But N is the midpoint of CD so that $ND = 1$. Hence $ND = DA$ and so triangle NDA is an isosceles right-angled triangle. It follows from *each base angle of a right-angled isosceles triangle is 45°* that each of angles AND and DAN is 45°.

act
4H
l08

ict
.3A
l05

ict
4B
.06

Now AB is parallel to DC, because $ABCD$ is a rectangle, so that, using *alternate angles on parallel lines are equal*, we get $\angle CDB = \angle ABD$. Thus $\angle NDZ$, which is the same angle as $\angle CDB$, is also equal to $x°$.

Applying *the sum of the angles in a triangle is 180°* to triangle NDZ, we obtain

$$\angle DZN + \angle ZND + \angle NDZ = 180°,$$

and so

$$\angle DZN + 45° + x° = 180°.$$

Subtracting $x°$ from each side, we get

$$\angle DZN + 45° = 180° - x°$$

and then subtracting 45° from each side, we obtain

$$\angle DZN = 135° - x°.$$

2. We shall find angles in the three triangles ADC, BHE and AHB, shown shaded in figure 1 on the following page.

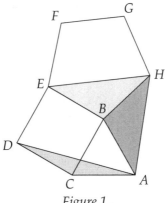

Figure 1

Now triangle ABC is equilateral, $BEDC$ is a square, and $BHGFE$ is a regular pentagon, therefore:

> $DC = CA$ because they are each equal to CB;
> $AB = BE$ because they are each equal to BC; and
> $HB = BA$ because they are each equal to BE.

Hence each of the triangles ADC, BHE and AHB is isosceles.

Since triangle ABC is equilateral and $BEDC$ is a square, $\angle DCA = 90° + 60°$, which is $150°$. But triangle ADC is isosceles, so that, using *the angles opposite equal sides of a triangle are equal*, we have $\angle ADC = \angle CAD$. Now applying *the sum of the angles in a triangle is 180°* to triangle ADC, we get

$$\angle ADC + \angle CAD + \angle DCA = 180°$$

so that

$$2 \times \angle ADC + 150° = 180°.$$

Subtracting $150°$ from each side, we get

$$2 \times \angle ADC = 180° - 150°$$
$$= 30°.$$

Finally, dividing each side by 2, we obtain

$$\angle ADC = 15°.$$

Also, $BEDC$ is a square, so that $\angle EDC = 90°$. Therefore

$$\angle EDA = 90° - \angle ADC$$
$$= 90° - 15°$$
$$= 75°. \tag{1}$$

Now the pentagon $BHGFE$ is regular, so that, from *the size of each exterior angle of a regular polygon with n sides is equal to* $360° \div n$, each exterior angle is equal to $360° \div 5 = 72°$. Therefore, using *the sum of the angles on a straight line is 180°*, we find that $\angle EBH = 180° - 72° = 108°$.

But triangle EBH is isosceles, so that we may use *the angles opposite equal sides of a triangle are equal* and *the sum of the angles in a triangle is 180°*, just as we did above when finding $\angle ADC$, to obtain $2 \times \angle BHE = 180° - 108° = 72°$ and thus $\angle BHE = 36°$.

Consider the angles at the point B. Using *the sum of the angles round a point is 360°*, we get

$$\angle HBA + \angle EBH + \angle CBE + \angle ABC = 360°.$$

Hence

$$\angle HBA + 108° + 90° + 60° = 360°,$$

so that

$$\angle HBA + 258° = 360°.$$

Subtracting 258° from each side, we obtain

$$\angle HBA = 360° - 258°$$
$$= 102°.$$

Once again triangle AHB is isosceles, so we may use *the angles opposite equal sides of a triangle are equal* and *the sum of the angles in a triangle is 180°*, just as we did above when finding $\angle ADC$, to obtain $2 \times \angle AHB = 180° - 102°$, which equals 78°, and thus $\angle AHB = 39°$. However, $\angle AHE = \angle AHB + \angle BHE$, so that

$$\angle AHE = 36° + 39°$$
$$= 75°. \tag{2}$$

We see from equations (1) and (2) that each of the angles $\angle EDA$ and $\angle AHE$ is equal to 75°, and so neither angle is the larger.

act
7.5I
112

act
.2B
104

act
.4D
107

act
.4B
106

act
.2A
104

ct
4D
07

ct
4B
06

3. Join D to B, as shown in the following figure.

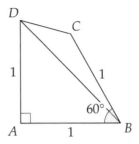

Now triangle ABD is an isosceles right-angled triangle with $DA = AB$. It follows from *each base angle of a right-angled isosceles triangle is 45°* that each of angles ABD and BDA is 45°.

But

$$\angle ABD + \angle DBC = \angle ABC$$

so that

$$45° + \angle DBC = 60°.$$

Subtracting 45° from each side, we get

$$\angle DBC = 60° - 45°$$
$$= 15°. \tag{1}$$

Now join A to C instead, as shown in the following figure.

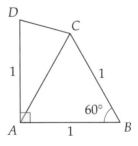

Then triangle ABC is equilateral, from *a triangle is equilateral when one angle is equal to 60° and the arms of the angle are equal*, because $\angle ABC = 60°$ and the sides AB and BC are equal.

Thus $AC = 1$ and so triangle CDA is isosceles, with $DA = AC$. Using *the angles opposite equal sides of a triangle are equal*, we obtain

$\angle CDA = \angle ACD$. Also, $\angle CAB = 60°$, so that $\angle DAC = 90° - 60°$, which is $30°$. Now applying *the sum of the angles in a triangle is 180°* to triangle CDA, we get

$$\angle CDA + \angle ACD + \angle DAC = 180°$$

so that

$$2 \times \angle CDA + 30° = 180°.$$

Subtracting $30°$ from each side, we get

$$2 \times \angle CDA = 180° - 30°$$
$$= 150°.$$

Finally, dividing each side by 2, we obtain

$$\angle CDA = 75°.$$

But

$$\angle CDB + \angle BDA = \angle CDA$$

so that

$$\angle CDB + 45° = 75°.$$

Subtracting $45°$ from each side, we get

$$\angle CDB = 75° - 45°$$
$$= 30°. \tag{2}$$

We see from equations (1) and (2) that $\angle CDB = 2 \times \angle DBC$, as required.

4.

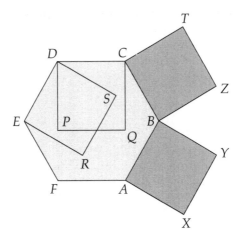

The hexagon $ABCDEF$ is regular, so the sides are all equal in length.

> Of course, being a regular polygon means more that. We shall use the angles later.

Therefore the four given squares all have the same size, with sides equal in length to those of the hexagon. In particular, $ZB = BY = SD = DP$.

Now we know that each angle at a vertex of a regular hexagon is equal to 120°, from the idea discussed in "Angles of a regular polygon" on page 112, and each angle at a vertex of a square is equal to 90°.

Using *the sum of the angles round a point is 360°* at B, we get

$$\angle ABC + \angle CBZ + \angle ZBY + \angle YBA = 360°$$

so that

$$120° + 90° + \angle ZBY + 90° = 360°.$$

Hence

$$300° + \angle ZBY = 360°.$$

Therefore, subtracting 300° from each side, we obtain

$$\angle ZBY = 60°.$$

Hence triangle ZBY is equilateral, from *a triangle is equilateral when one angle is equal to 60° and the arms of the angle are equal,* because $\angle ZBY = 60°$ and $ZB = BY$.

Also, we have

$$\angle CDE = \angle CDS + \angle SDE$$
$$= (\angle CDP - \angle SDP) + \angle SDE$$

so that

$$120° = 90° - \angle SDP + 90°$$
$$= 180° - \angle SDP.$$

Subtracting 120° from each side, we get

$$0° = 60° - \angle SDP$$

and then adding $\angle SDP$ to each side, we obtain

$$\angle SDP = 60°.$$

Therefore, because $SD = DP$, triangle SDP is equilateral, from *a triangle is equilateral when one angle is equal to 60° and the arms of the angle are equal.*

Hence each of the triangles DPS and ZBY is equilateral. But $DP = BY$, so that the triangles have the same size, and thus all six sides are equal in length. In particular, $PS = YZ$.

> We did not need to prove that the two triangles are equilateral: it would be sufficient to prove that they are congruent, which may be done using the SAS test for congruency (fact 17.4K on page 109).
>
> However, it is just as quick to prove that the triangles are equilateral and equal, since two pairs of sides are all equal and two appropriate angles are 60°, as we have shown.

5. How many vertices of the original polygon P can the cut pass through? Since P is convex (see section 17.5 on page 109), there are only three possibilities (see the following figures): the cut passes through two vertices, or one vertex, or no vertices.

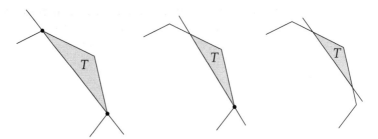

Let us label the vertices of the triangle A, B and C and then deal with each case in turn.

Two vertices of P on the cut

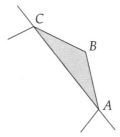

In this case, all the points A, B and C are vertices of polygon P, but only A and C are vertices of polygon Q. All the unlabelled vertices are the same in both polygons. Therefore P has one more vertex than Q. Hence P has one more edge than Q, so that

$$m = n - 1.$$

One vertex of P on the cut

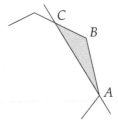

In this case, point A is a vertex of both P and Q, point B is a vertex of P but not of Q, and point C is a vertex of Q but not of P. All the unlabelled vertices are the same in both polygons. Therefore P and Q have the same number of vertices. Hence P and Q have the same number of edges, so that

$$m = n.$$

No vertices of P on the cut

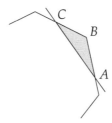

In this case, point B is a vertex of P but not of Q, and points A and C are vertices of Q but not of P. All the unlabelled vertices are the same in both polygons. Therefore Q has one more vertex than P. Hence Q has one more edge than P, so that

$$m = n + 1.$$

To summarise, the relationship between m and n is that

$$m = n - 1,$$
$$m = n,$$
$$\text{or} \quad m = n + 1.$$

Note that the answer is exactly the same for every convex polygon whether or not it is regular.

6.

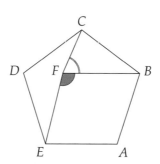

We have deliberately drawn F in the wrong place in the above diagram, so that EFC does not appear to be a straight line. This should help to stop us making incorrect assumptions.

Our plan is to calculate (separately) the two marked angles.

Firstly, using *the size of each exterior angle of a regular polygon with n sides is equal to* $360° \div n$, we find that each exterior angle of a regular pentagon is $360° \div 5 = 72°$, and therefore each interior angle is $108°$, using *the sum of the angles on a straight line is 180°*. In particular, $\angle EAB = 108°$ and $\angle ABC = 108°$.

Now $ABFE$ is a rhombus, so using *the opposite angles of a parallelogram are equal*, we obtain $\angle BFE = \angle EAB$ and therefore $\angle BFE = 108°$.

Because BF and AE are parallel, it follows from *the sum of allied angles on parallel lines is 180°* that $\angle ABF + \angle EAB = 180°$ so that $\angle ABF = 72°$. But $\angle FBC = \angle ABC - \angle ABF$ and hence

$$\angle FBC = 108° - 72°$$
$$= 36°.$$

Also, because $ABFE$ is a rhombus, the sides are equal, and hence $BF = BA$. But the pentagon is regular, so that $BA = BC$, and therefore $BF = BC$. Now we apply *the angles opposite equal sides of a triangle are equal* to isosceles triangle BCF to obtain $\angle BCF = \angle CFB$. However, we found above that $\angle FBC = 36°$, so we may calculate $\angle CFB$ from *the sum of the angles in a triangle is 180°* in triangle FBC:

$$\angle CFB = \tfrac{1}{2}(180° - 36°)$$
$$= 72°.$$

Finally, because

$$\angle BFE + \angle CFB = 108° + 72°$$
$$= 180°,$$

we may use the fact that *if two angles share one arm and sum to 180°, then the other arms form a straight line* to deduce that EFC is a straight line.

7. Figure 1 shows an example of such a pentagon, and figure 2 shows how four of the pentagons in figure 1 fit together to form a hexagon.

Fac
17.5
p 11

Fac
17.2
p 10

Fac
17.5
p 11

Fac
17.3
p 10

Fa
17.4
p 1

Fa
17.
p 1

Fa
17.
p 1

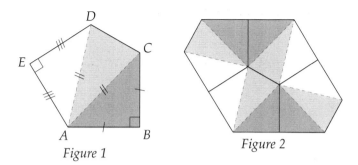

Figure 1

Figure 2

How do we know that the pentagons fit together in the manner shown in figure 2? We need to show that the edges are all straight lines and that there are no 'holes' or 'overlaps' in the interior of the new shape.

Along the outside, there are four points where two pentagons meet, indicated in figure 3. But at each such point the interior angles of the pentagons are both 90° (corresponding to vertices B and E in figure 1), so the edges of the pentagons form a straight line, as required.

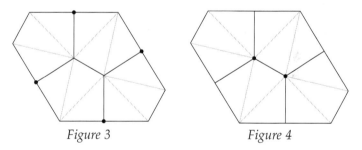

Figure 3

Figure 4

The only points left to deal with are the two inside the hexagon, indicated in figure 4, where three pentagons meet.

Consider one such point. The pentagons will fit together if all the angles at the point add up to 360°. As indicated in figure 5 on the next page, three of the angles correspond to the angles of triangle ACD in figure 1. Hence the sum of these three angles is 180°.

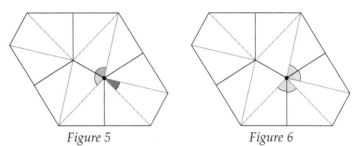

Figure 5   *Figure 6*

We now deal with the four angles marked in figure 6.

Now triangle *ABC* in figure 1 is an isosceles right-angled triangle, with *AB = BC*. Therefore angles *CAB* and *BCA* are equal to 45°, from *each base angle of a right-angled isosceles triangle is 45°*. Similarly, angles *EAD* and *ADE* are equal to 45°.

Therefore each angle marked in figure 6 is equal to 45°, so that the sum of the four angles is 180°. Hence the sum of all the angles at the marked point is 180° + 180° = 360°, as required.

> We have not used the fact that *AC = AD* (apart from in our figures). Indeed, this condition is not required: the resulting pentagon is no longer symmetrical, but it is still possible to fit four of them together to make a hexagon, as the following figure shows.

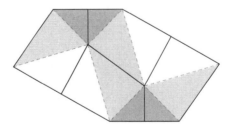

8. From *the size of each exterior angle of a regular polygon with n sides is equal to 360° ÷ n*, each exterior angle of a regular 20-sided polygon equals 360° ÷ 20 = 18°. From *the sum of the angles on a straight line is 180°*, the interior angle therefore equals 180° − 18° = 162°.

Similarly, the exterior angle of a regular pentagon is equal to 360° ÷ 5 = 72°, so the interior angle is equal to 180° − 72° = 108°.

Fac
17.4
p 1(

Fa
17
p ▌
Fa
17
p ▌

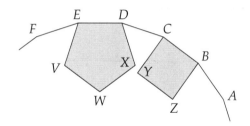

Therefore

$$\angle YCD = \angle BCD - \angle BCY$$
$$= 162° - 90°$$
$$= 72°,$$

and

$$\angle CDX = \angle CDE - \angle XDE$$
$$= 162° - 108°$$
$$= 54°.$$

Now the sides BC and CY of the square are equal in length, and the sides BC and CD of the icosagon are equal in length. Therefore $CY = CD$ and the triangle CDY is isosceles. Using *the angles opposite equal sides of a triangle are equal*, we get $\angle CDY = \angle DYC$.

Using *the sum of the angles in a triangle is 180°*, we obtain

$$\angle CYD + \angle CDY + \angle YCD = 180°$$

so that

$$2 \times \angle CDY + 72° = 180°.$$

Subtracting 72° from each side, we get

$$2 \times \angle CDY = 108°$$

and finally, dividing both sides by 2, we obtain

$$\angle CDY = 54°.$$

Therefore each of the angles $\angle CDY$ and $\angle CDX$ is equal to 54°, which is only possible if they are the same angle and the point X lies on the line DY.

9. Let $\angle BAJ = x°$.

> Introducing a letter allows us to use some algebra in order to explain our solution clearly.

Then, because the squares are 'equally spread', $\angle EAD = x°$ and $\angle HAG = x°$.

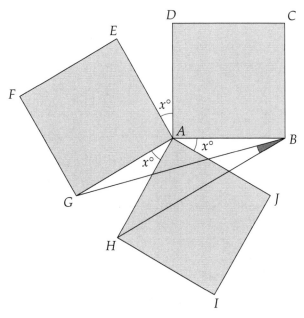

Now the angle at the vertex of a square is 90°, so applying *the sum of the angles round a point is 360°* to the point A, we get

$$x° + 90° + x° + 90° + x° + 90° = 360°,$$

so that, gathering terms and subtracting 270° from each side, we obtain

$$3x° = 360° - 270°$$
$$= 90°.$$

Dividing by 3, we get

$$x = 30°.$$

In the triangle BAG, we have $\angle BAG = x° + 90° + x°$, which from the last result is $150°$. Also $BA = AG$, because they are sides of identical squares, and so triangle BAG is isosceles. Therefore, using *the angles opposite equal sides of a triangle are equal*, we obtain $\angle GBA = \angle AGB$. Now, using *the sum of the angles in a triangle is 180°*, we get

$$\angle BAG + \angle GBA + \angle AGB = 180°,$$

so that

$$150° + \angle GBA + \angle GBA = 180°$$

and so, subtracting $150°$ from each side, we obtain

$$2 \times \angle GBA = 30°.$$

Dividing by 2, we get

$$\angle GBA = 15°.$$

In the same way, $BA = AH$ (so that triangle BAH is isosceles) and therefore, using *the angles opposite equal sides of a triangle are equal* again, we obtain $\angle HBA = \angle HBA$.

Now, using *the sum of the angles in a triangle is 180°* once more, we get

$$\angle BAH + \angle HBA + \angle AHB = 180°.$$

Therefore

$$120° + \angle HBA + \angle HBA = 180°$$

and so, subtracting $120°$ from each side, we obtain

$$2 \times \angle HBA = 60°.$$

Dividing by 2, we get

$$\angle HBA = 30°.$$

Finally,

$$\begin{aligned}
\angle HBG &= \angle HBA - \angle GBA \\
&= 30° - 15° \\
&= 15°.
\end{aligned}$$

act
7.4D
107
act
7.4B
106

act
.4D
107
act
.4B
106

Exercise 13

1. The only way to write 24 as a sum of five positive integers, each of which is at most 5, is $24 = 5 + 5 + 5 + 5 + 4$. We deduce that child A won four competitions and was second in the fifth.

   Child E scores 5 in competition W, so child E was first in W, and hence child A was second in W.

   Completing the table so far, including the fact that child D scores 4 in competition V, we get the following.

	V	W	X	Y	Z	Total
A	5	4	5	5	5	24
B						
C						
D	4					
E		5	3			

   The total marks available in each of the five competitions is $1 + 2 + 3 + 4 + 5 = 15$. Hence the total of all the marks is $5 \times 15 = 75$. But the total for child A is 24. Therefore the total of the marks for the other four children is $75 - 24 = 51$.

   Now the total mark for child E is at least 11, since $1 + 5 + 3 + 1 + 1 = 11$. Thus the total mark for child D is least 12, that for child C is at least 13, and for child B it is at least 14. But $11 + 12 + 13 + 14 = 50$, so, since there are no ties, the only possibility is that the total mark for child B is 15, the total for child C is 13, the total for child D is 12 and that for child E is 11. The table is now as follows.

	V	W	X	Y	Z	Total
A	5	4	5	5	5	24
B						15
C						13
D	4					12
E	1	5	3	1	1	11

   The only information remaining unused is that child C scores the same in four competitions. But there are already two or more scores of 1, 4 and 5 in the table, so that child C can only score four 2s, or four 3s. However, $4 \times 2 = 8$, so that, in order to score four 2s, child C would need to score 5 in the fifth competition, which is impossible because there are already five 5s in the table.

We deduce that child C scores four 3s, and one 1 in order to give a total of 13. Also, the score of 1 can only be for competition X because 3 already appears in that column. The table is now as shown in table 1.

	V	W	X	Y	Z	Total
A	5	4	5	5	5	24
B						15
C	3	3	1	3	3	13
D	4					12
E	1	5	3	1	1	11

Table 1

	V	W	X	Y	Z	Total
A	5	4	5	5	5	24
B	2					15
C	3	3	1	3	3	13
D	4					12
E	1	5	3	1	1	11

Table 2

The missing mark in the V column is then clearly 2. Inserting this, we get table 2.

The eight missing marks in table 2 are one 1, four 2s, and three 4s. In order to get the odd total for child B, the missing 1 can only appear in this row. We now have table 3.

	V	W	X	Y	Z	Total
A	5	4	5	5	5	24
B	2	1				15
C	3	3	1	3	3	13
D	4	2				12
E	1	5	3	1	1	11

Table 3

	V	W	X	Y	Z	Total
A	5	4	5	5	5	24
B	2	1	4	4	4	15
C	3	3	1	3	3	13
D	4	2	2	2	2	12
E	1	5	3	1	1	11

Table 4

Finally, the only way to obtain the required totals is for child B to score 4, and for child D to score 2, in each of the last three competitions. Thus there is only one possibility, and the completed table is shown in table 4.

2. (a) The first twelve moves are shown by the numbered arrows in the figure.

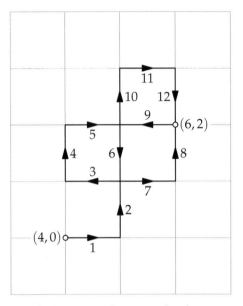

After 12 moves the bug is at the point $(6, 2)$.

(b) Notice that the bug starts facing East, and after six moves it is again facing East, having moved one unit East and one unit North. Therefore for each of the next six moves the value of $x - y$ is the same as for the equivalent move in the first six moves. Hence moves 7 to 12 repeat moves 1 to 6, just starting in a different place. The same is true for each subsequent sequence of six moves: the effect of each set of six moves is to shift one unit East and one unit North from the starting point, and to finish facing East again.

Now making 48 moves is the same as making 8 sets of six moves, so that after 48 moves the bug will have moved 8 units East and 8 units North. Since it starts at the point $(4, 0)$ the bug will therefore end at the point $(12, 8)$.

Moves 49 and 50 repeat moves 1 and 2, but starting at the point $(12, 8)$. Therefore after 50 moves the bug will be one point East and 1 point North of this, that is, at the point $(13, 9)$.

3. (a) On a 4×1 board, X can win by first placing a counter as shown in the following figure.

This leaves only single squares unoccupied, so that Y is then unable to make a move.

Therefore X wins on a 4×1 board.

(b) On a 5×1 board, X has essentially only two possible opening moves, as shown in the following figures. Any other opening move is a reflection of one of these.

In either case, there are two adjacent unoccupied squares, and Y may place a counter on these. By doing so, Y leaves only one unoccupied square, so that X is then unable to make a move.

Therefore Y wins on a 5×1 board.

(c) On a 6×1 board, X can win by first playing as shown in the following figure.

There are now two pairs of adjacent unoccupied squares. No matter which pair Y chooses, X can always place a counter on the other pair. This leaves no unoccupied squares, so that Y is then unable to make a move.

Therefore X wins on a 6×1 board.

(d) Player X also wins on an 8×1 board. One way for X to win is by first placing a counter in the middle of the board, as shown in the following figure (there are other winning first moves).

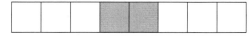

This leaves 3 unoccupied squares on either side. Now Y may place a counter in either set of 3 unoccupied squares. But whichever set Y chooses, X can always place a counter within the other set. By doing so, X leaves two separate unoccupied squares, so that Y is then unable to make a move.

Therefore X wins on an 8×1 board.

4. (a) X wins by first choosing 2. After this, X arranges to make the total equal to 5, 8, 11, 14, 17 and finally 20—thus winning—by adopting the following strategy:

add 1 when Y adds 2;

add 2 when Y adds 1.

By adopting this strategy, X ensures that 3 is always added to whatever the total was before Y's move.

(b) Firstly, we observe that a player who makes the total equal to 15 will win, because whatever the opponent adds to the total (1, 2 or 4), the player can then add 4 to make the total 20 or more, thereby winning.

Secondly, we note that a player who makes the total equal to 12 will win, because the player can then adopt the following strategy:

add 1 when the opponent adds 2;

add 2 when the opponent adds 1;

add 4 when the opponent adds 4.

By adopting this strategy, the player either makes the total equal to 15 (which we know is a winning position) or makes the total equal to 20, thereby winning.

A winning strategy is therefore "always make the total equal to a multiple of 3, that is, 3, 6, 9, ... until a total of either 12 or 15 is reached". This is possible by adopting the following strategy:

add 1 when the opponent adds 2;

add 2 when the opponent adds 1 or 4.

By adopting this strategy, the player always adds 3 or 6 to whatever the total was before the opponent's move. If this total was a multiple of 3, then the new total will be a multiple of 3.

But on the first move, X cannot choose a multiple of 3. However, whatever X chooses on the first move, Y can always make the total 3 or 6, and then adopt the above strategy. Therefore Y can always win.

5. (a) Firstly, note that we are free to choose the tile in the opposite corner—shown shaded in the figure 1—in any way we like; the tile can be A, B, C or D, and in each case tiles can be chosen for the other squares. However, once we have selected this tile, the edge-matching stipulation in the question means that there is one and only one choice for each of the other two tiles, as shown in figure 2.

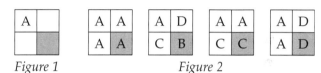

Figure 1   *Figure 2*

We observe two things:

however the diagonal tiles are chosen, the grid may be completely tiled;

once the diagonal tiles have been chosen, there is only one way to complete the tiling.

There are four different ways when the top-left tile is tile A. Similarly there are four different ways for each other choice of top-left tile. Since the top-left tile can be chosen in four ways, altogether there are $4 \times 4 = 16$ different ways of covering the 2×2 grid with four tiles.

(b) Consider the diagonal shown shaded in figure 3 (note that we could equally well have used the other diagonal).

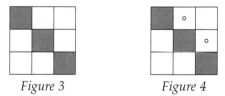

Figure 3   *Figure 4*

We are free to choose each of the three tiles along the diagonal in any way we like; each tile can be A, B, C or D. However, once these tiles are selected, there is one and only one choice for each of the other tiles. For example, two edges of each of the tiles marked in figure 4 meets a diagonal tile, so each marked tile is determined. By the same argument, the tile in the top right is also determined because two of its edges meet a marked tile.

We make two observations:

> however the diagonal tiles are chosen, the grid may be completely tiled;
>
> once the diagonal tiles have been chosen, there is only one way to complete the tiling.

Since there are four ways to choose each of the diagonal tiles, altogether there are $4 \times 4 \times 4$ different ways of covering the 3×3 grid with tiles.

(c) We may generalise the argument of part (b) to deal with the $n \times n$ grid: we are free to choose each of the diagonal tiles in any way we like; but once these tiles are selected all the other tiles are determined. So altogether there are

$$4 \times 4 \times 4 \times \cdots \times 4 = 4^n$$

different ways of covering the $n \times n$ grid with tiles.

6. Let us call a position *equal-gap* when the 'gap' (the number of empty squares) between A and B is the same as the gap between C and D. We observe that:

   (i) from an equal-gap position, whatever move a player makes will leave a position which is not equal-gap;

   (ii) from a position which is not equal-gap, it is always possible to move to an equal-gap position.

Thus a player who moves to an equal-gap position will be able to do so again next time, whatever move the opponent makes. And the opponent is forced to move to a position which is not an equal-gap position. But the final (winning) position is equal-gap. Therefore a winning strategy is "always move to an equal-gap position".

But initially the first player can move counter A two squares to the right, thereby making the gap between A and B equal to the gap between C and D. In other words, on the opening move the first player can move to an equal-gap position (this is possible because the initial position is not equal-gap).

Whatever the second player now does, the first player can once again move to an equal-gap position. The process repeats, so that, by adopting the strategy "always move to an equal-gap position", the first player can ensure that they win the game.

7. (a) One way is to colour the four cells shown in the following figure.

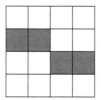

We can show that the L-shaped piece cannot be placed on the grid without covering at least one coloured cell by just testing each of the twelve possible positions.

(b) Divide the grid into four L-shaped regions, as shown in the following figure.

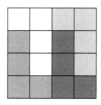

Suppose that at most three cells are coloured red. In whatever way this is done, because there are four regions, at least one of the regions does not contain a red cell. Hence it is possible to place an L-shaped piece on the grid without it covering a red cell, by placing it in this region.

Therefore it is impossible to achieve the required outcome by colouring fewer than four cells red.

8. Place the integers in five groups, with four integers in each group, as shown below.

Group	Integers
A	1, 6, 11, 16
B	2, 7, 12, 17
C	3, 8, 13, 18
D	4, 9, 14, 19
E	5, 10, 15, 20

> We observe that all the relevant integers are included, but that the groups are distinct, that is, the groups are completely different from each other—no integer appears in more than one group. Therefore what we choose from one group does not affect what we may choose from another—the choices are independent.
>
> We also observe that two integers from different groups never differ by 5, so we only need to worry about choosing integers from the *same* group.

Whichever integer we choose first from a group, we may always choose a second integer from the same group that does not differ by 5 from the first. However, after choosing two such integers from a group, both the remaining ones differ by 5 from at least one of them. Thus we may always choose two integers from the same group, but we may never choose more than two. For example, from group A we may choose 1 and 11, or 1 and 16, or 6 and 16.

There are five groups and we may choose at most two from each, so the largest value of n is $5 \times 2 = 10$.

Now there are 3 ways of choosing a pair of integers from each group, as illustrated above for group A. We need to choose a pair from each of five groups, so using *the multiplication principle*, a list of ten integers may be chosen in $3 \times 3 \times 3 \times 3 \times 3 = 243$ ways.

> Note that this method finds the number of lists without actually finding the lists themselves. Attempting to write out

> these lists would not be a good idea, as described in the idea discussed in "Counting" on page 121.

9. Firstly, we observe that the last digit cannot be even or 5, since then the last two digits would not form a two-digit prime. Similarly, no middle digit can be even or 5; indeed the only digit that can be even or 5 is the first.

There are ten two-digit prime numbers with two odd digits that do not include 5:

$$11, \ 13, \ 17, \ 19, \ 31, \ 37, \ 71, \ 73, \ 79 \text{ and } 97. \tag{*}$$

A 'chain' containing all of the primes in the list (*) will be a larger integer than one which does not contain them all.

We create a network connecting the digits 1, 3, 7 and 9 as follows. For each prime '*ab*' in the list (*), we draw an arrow from the digit *a* to the digit *b*. For example, 19 is in the list, so we draw an arrow from 1 to 9. The following figure shows the resulting network.

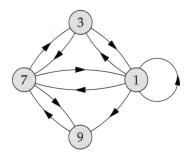

Each arrow corresponds to a prime in the list (*), so to use all the primes in the list we need to find a chain that follows *all* the arrows. However, two arrows go to 9 but only one comes from 9. Thus a chain using all the arrows necessarily ends at 9. Similarly, such a chain necessarily starts at 1, because four arrows come from 1 but only three go to 1.

Consider the chain 19 737 131 179, which uses all the arrows. At each stage the chain follows the arrow to the largest possible digit. Hence the chain gives the largest possible integer containing each prime in the list (*).

Which digit can be placed at the front of a chain starting with 1, so that the first two digits form a two-digit prime? We know that the digit is even or 5, but 81 is not prime, so that the digit is not 8 (the largest possible). However, the next largest possible digit is 6, and 61 *is* prime.

Thus 619 737 131 179 is the largest number of the required form.

10. The smallest number of white cells is four. One way to achieve this is to visit the four white cells marked in the following figure.

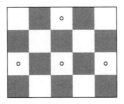

We need to prove that four is the smallest number, in other words, that it is not possible to visit fewer than four white squares.

Notice that from any white square, the maximum number of black squares that can be visited is four. Therefore, when at most three white squares are visited, at most $3 \times 4 = 12$ black squares can be visited. However, at least two of these black squares will be "shared", in order to connect the route. Therefore the route can visit at most 10 black squares.

But there are exactly 10 black squares in the grid. Therefore, when at most three white squares are visited, there need to be exactly three of them, and each has to "connect" to the maximum number of four black squares. However, in order to visit the black square in the lower left corner of the grid, one of the white squares adjoining the corner has to be visited, and each of these white squares only connects to *three* black squares. Therefore it is impossible to visit all the black squares when at most three white squares are visited.

Exercise 14

1. Join O to B to form the triangles OAB and OBC.

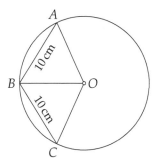

Then

$$OA = OB \qquad \text{(each is a radius),}$$
$$AB = BC \qquad \text{(each equals 10 cm)}$$
$$\text{and} \quad OB = OC \qquad \text{(each is a radius).}$$

Hence triangles OAB and OBC are congruent, from *the SSS test for congruency.*

Therefore the area of triangle OAB is half the area of the quadrilateral $OABC$, so is equal to half of 120 cm^2, which is 60 cm^2.

Now triangle OAB has two sides which are the radius of the circle and is therefore isosceles. Let X be the midpoint of AB and let the length of the radius of the circle be r cm, as shown in the following figure.

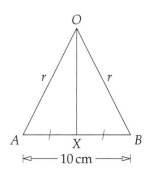

From the result *the median through the vertex angle of an isosceles tri-*

angle meets the opposite side at right angles, we know that angle OXA is a right angle, and so OX is the height of triangle OAB.

Using *the area of a triangle is equal to $\frac{1}{2} \times base \times height$*, and knowing that the length of the base AB is 10 cm, we obtain

Fac
18.2
p 11

$$60 = \tfrac{1}{2} \times 10 \times OX,$$

so that

$$60 = 5 \times OX.$$

Dividing both sides by 5, we get

$$12 = OX.$$

Then, using *Pythagoras' theorem* in right-angled triangle OAX, we obtain

Fac
18.2
p 1

$$r^2 = AX^2 + XO^2$$
$$= 5^2 + 12^2$$
$$= 25 + 144$$
$$= 169$$
$$= 13^2.$$

Therefore $r = 13$ and so the length of the radius of the circle is 13 cm.

2. Add two lines, each passing through the given point and parallel to a side of the parallelogram, as shown in the following figure.

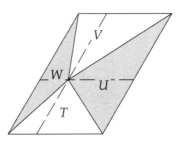

These lines divide the parallelogram into four smaller parallelograms because each of these quadrilaterals has two pairs of parallel sides.

Now consider each of these smaller parallelograms. We know that *a parallelogram is cut by a diagonal into two congruent triangles*, so that

F
17
P

the area of each small parallelogram is divided by its diagonal into two equal parts, one grey, one white.

It follows that the total area of the grey regions is equal to the total area of the white regions. In other words, that

$$\text{area } T + \text{area } V = \text{area } U + \text{area } W.$$

3. Let the side of the square have length 4 (see section 18.1).

Then the area of the square $ABCD$ is 4×4, which equals 16, and ST has length 2.

Let the centre of the circle, which is also the centre of the square, be O, and consider the triangle TOS (see the following figure). This triangle is isosceles because each of TO and OS is a radius of the circle and so $TO = OS$.

Draw the median from O to meet ST at M, as shown. From the result *the median through the vertex angle of an isosceles triangle meets the opposite side at right angles* we know that OM is the perpendicular bisector of ST.

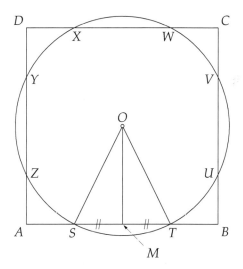

Now O is the centre of the square $ABCD$ and so the length of MO is half the length of the side of the square. Therefore MO has length 2. The triangle SMO is right-angled at M and $SM = \frac{1}{2}ST$ so that SM has length 1.

Using *Pythagoras' theorem* in triangle SMO, we obtain

Fac
18.2
p 11

$$OS^2 = SM^2 + MO^2$$
$$= 1^2 + 2^2$$
$$= 5$$

so that

$$OS = \sqrt{5}.$$

The radius of the circle is therefore $\sqrt{5}$. Then, using *the area of a circle of radius r is equal to πr^2*, we have

Fac
18.3
p 12

$$\text{area of the circle} = \pi\left(\sqrt{5}\right)^2$$
$$= \pi \times \sqrt{5} \times \sqrt{5}$$
$$= 5\pi.$$

But 5π is less than 5×3.2, which is equal to 16. It follows that the area of the circle is less than the area of the square.

Hence the area of the square is larger than the area of the circle.

4. The area required is shown shaded in figure 1. Now the original triangle ABC is equilateral, so that its sides are equal in length. But one side of each of the three squares is a side of this triangle, so the squares have the same size. Hence each of the triangles QAR, UBP and SCT is isosceles, because $QA = AR$, $UB = BP$ and $SC = CT$.

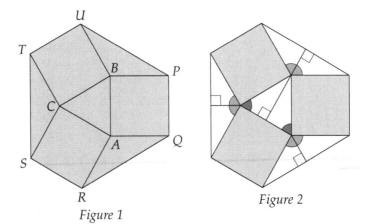

Figure 1

Figure 2

Furthermore, from the fact that triangle ABC is equilateral, and using *the sum of the angles round a point is 360°* at each of the points A, B and C, the 'top' angle in each of these three isosceles triangles is $360° - 90° - 90° - 60° = 120°$.

Now draw the medians of these isosceles triangles from A, B and C, and draw the median of triangle ABC from B. Using the result *the median through the vertex angle of an isosceles triangle meets the opposite side at right angles*, we obtain figure 2. We claim that figure 2 divides the whole area into three squares and eight congruent right-angled triangles.

Why are the triangles congruent? Well, each triangle has a side of the square as hypotenuse. What about the marked angles? Two of them are equal to 60° because triangle ABC is equilateral. Each other marked angle is equal to 60° using *the median through the vertex angle of an isosceles triangle bisects that angle* for each of the isosceles triangles QAR, UBP and SCT. Each triangle is also right-angled. Therefore the eight triangles are congruent, from *the AAS test for congruency*.

From figure 2, the area required is equal to the sum of the areas of the three squares and the areas of the eight triangles. But each square has area 4, so that altogether the three squares have area $3 \times 4 = 12$.

Also, the central two triangles form the equilateral triangle ABC, whose sides have length 2. We may use *an equilateral triangle with sides of length 2 has height $\sqrt{3}$* and *the area of a triangle is equal to $\frac{1}{2} \times base \times height$* to find the area of this equilateral triangle. We deduce that the total area of two of the eight triangles is equal to

$$\tfrac{1}{2} \times 2 \times \sqrt{3} = \sqrt{3}.$$

Thus the area of all eight triangles is $4 \times \sqrt{3}$ and so the area required is equal to $12 + 4\sqrt{3}$.

Fact
7.2A
104

Fact
7.4F
108

Fact
.4G
108

Fact
.4J
109

Fact
2D
18

Fact
2A
16

5.

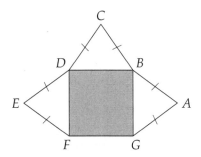

The shaded region $BDFG$ is a square; it follows that $GB = BD = DF$. In the triangles GAB, BCD and DEF, we therefore have

$$GA = BC = DE,$$
$$AB = CD = EF$$
$$\text{and} \quad BG = DB = FD.$$

Hence these triangles have sides of equal length and are therefore congruent, from *the SSS test for congruency*.

Now we are told that the area of the whole polygon is exactly twice the area of $BDFG$. Thus the total area of these three triangles is equal to the area of the square $BDFG$, which is $6^2 = 36$. Therefore the area of each triangle is $\frac{1}{3} \times 36 = 12$.

Let the height of one of the triangles be h. Then, using *the area of a triangle is equal to $\frac{1}{2} \times base \times height$*, we obtain

$$12 = \tfrac{1}{2} \times 6 \times h$$
$$= 3h.$$

Dividing both sides by 3, we get

$$4 = h.$$

Now consider the triangle BCD, which is isosceles because $BC = CD$. Using the result *the median through the vertex angle of an isosceles triangle meets the opposite side at right angles*, we know that the median is the height, as shown in the following figure.

Fa
17.
p 1

Fa
18.
p 1

Fa
17
p

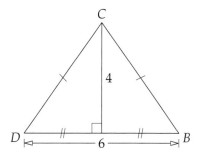

act
.2B
116

Now applying *Pythagoras' theorem* to half of triangle BCD, we get

$$CD^2 = 3^4 + 4^2$$
$$= 9 + 16$$
$$= 25$$
$$= 5^2.$$

Therefore $CD = 5$.

> Alternatively, we could observe that half of triangle BCD is a 3-4-5 triangle.

Thus GA, AB, BC, DE and EF are also equal to 5.

Hence the perimeter of the polygon is $5 + 5 + 5 + 5 + 5 + 5 + 6 = 36$.

6. We shall show that the shaded area in the given figure is equal to the unshaded area.

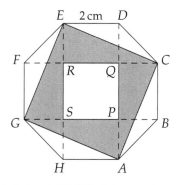

Consider the quadrilateral $BCQP$. We are given that the sides PQ and BC are parallel, and the sides CQ and BP are parallel because the opposite sides of the square $PQRS$ are parallel. Thus $BCQP$ is a parallelogram, so that $BC = PQ$ from the fact that *the opposite sides of a parallelogram are equal in length*. In other words, the side lengths of the square $PQRS$ and the octagon are the same.

Fac 17.5. p 11

Let X be the point where HA and CB meet (see the following figure).

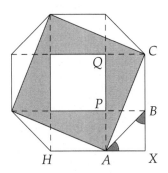

We are given that XC and AQ are parallel, and CQ and XA are parallel. Thus $AXCQ$ is a parallelogram. Furthermore, the areas of triangles ACQ and CAX are equal, from the result that *a parallelogram is cut by a diagonal into two congruent triangles*.

Fa 17.5 p 1

But triangle CAX is made up of triangles CAB and BAX, so that the area of triangle ACQ is equal to the sum of the areas of triangles CAB and BAX.

Now $\angle XBA$ and $\angle BAX$ are exterior angles of the octagon, so each is equal to $45°$ from *the size of each exterior angle of a regular polygon with n sides is equal to $360° \div n$*. Thus in triangle BAX, two angles are $45°$ and the side BA between them is an edge of the octagon.

Fa 17. p 1

However, the square $PQRS$ is divided by its diagonals into four such triangles, as shown in the following figure—each triangle in the figure has two angles equal to $45°$, and the side between them is equal to the length of an edge of the octagon, as shown above.

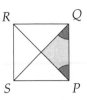

Fact
7.4J
109

Hence triangle BAX is congruent to each of the four triangles in the figure, using *the AAS test for congruency*. The area of triangle BAX is therefore equal to one quarter of the area of the square $PQRS$. Thus the area of the shaded triangle ACQ is equal to the area of triangle ABC and one quarter of the area of the square $PQRS$.

Since we can do the same thing for each of the shaded trangles ACQ, CER, EGS and GAP, we conclude that the shaded area in the given figure is equal to the sum of the areas of the four triangles like CAB and the area of the square $PQRS$.

Therefore we have proved that the shaded and unshaded areas in the given figure are equal. Hence half of the entire octagon is shaded.

> In this case, we could solve the problem in a different way by actually finding the shaded area and the area of the octagon.

7. Consider one pane of glass, and add a diagonal dividing it into two parts, as shown in figure 1.

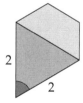
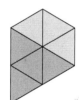

Figure 1   *Figure 2*

One part of the divided pane has two sides of length 2, and six panes fit together round a point to make the window, so the angle marked in figure 1 is $360° \div 6$, that is, $60°$. Hence, from the fact that *a triangle is equilateral when one angle is equal to $60°$ and the arms of the angle are equal*, this part is an equilateral triangle with sides of length 2. Thus we may divide this part into four small equilateral triangles, using *an equilateral triangle may be dissected into four equilateral triangles*. Also, the diagonal is the third side of the triangle so has length 2.

Fact
4C
107

Fact
6A
13

Fact
6B
13

The other part of the divided pane is half a regular hexagon, so may be dissected into three small equilateral triangles, using *a regular hexagon may be dissected into six equilateral triangles*. Because the diagonal has length 2 the sides of these triangles have length 1.

Therefore each pane may be divided into seven small equilateral triangles, as shown in figure 2.

Since there are six panes, the whole window may therefore be dissected into 42 small equilateral triangles.

Each equilateral triangle has sides of length 1, so the height of each triangle is $\frac{1}{2}\sqrt{3}$ from the fact that *an equilateral triangle with sides of length 2 has height* $\sqrt{3}$.

Thus, using *the area of a triangle is equal to* $\frac{1}{2} \times$ *base* $\times$ *height*, we find that the area of one equilateral triangle is

$$\tfrac{1}{2} \times 1 \times \tfrac{1}{2}\sqrt{3} = \tfrac{1}{4}\sqrt{3}.$$

Hence the total area of the window is

$$42 \times \tfrac{1}{4}\sqrt{3} = \frac{21}{2}\sqrt{3}.$$

8. The points E and F are the points of trisection of the line DA. Now FJ and EI are parallel to KD and I and J are the points of trisection of the line KA. By joining F, E, I and J to the points of trisection of the line KD, we see that triangle AKD may be dissected into nine congruent triangles—triangle AEI and eight others—each of which is congruent to triangle AKD, as shown in the following figure.

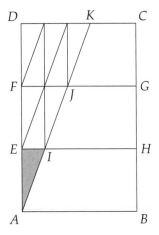

Since $JKDF$ has been divided into 5 of these triangles, it follows that the area of $JKDF$ is equal to 5 times the area of one such triangle.

But *JK* divides *CDFG* into two parts of equal area, so the area of *CDFG* is equal to 10 times the area of one triangle.

However, the area of *CDFG* is one third of the area of the whole rectangle *ABCD*. Therefore the area of *ABCD* is equal to 30 times the area of one triangle.

Hence the area of triangle *AEI* is $\frac{1}{30}$ of the area of *ABCD*.

9. The area of the curvy unshaded region in figure 2 is equal to the area of the whole star-shaped region minus the shaded area.

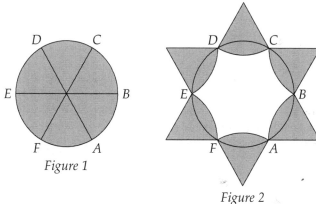

Figure 1

Figure 2

But the shaded area in figure 2 is the same as the shaded area in figure 1, that is, the area of the circle. The radius of the circle is 1, so that, using *the area of a circle of radius r is equal to πr^2*, we find that the shaded area is equal to $\pi \times 1^2$, which equals π.

Now the points *A*, *B*, *C*, *D*, *E* and *F* are equally spaced around the circle, so that *ABCDEF* is a regular hexagon. Using the fact that *a regular hexagon may be dissected into six equilateral triangles*, we may divide the hexagon into equilateral triangles, each of which is turned outside the circle when the sectors are rearranged. Thus the whole star-shaped region may be divided into equilateral triangles, as shown in figure 3 on the following page.

ct
3D
20

ct
6B
13

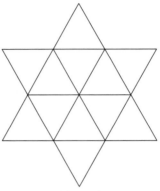

Figure 3

There are twelve equilateral triangles, each with sides of length 1 (the radius of the circle).

Using *an equilateral triangle with sides of length 2 has height* $\sqrt{3}$*,* we find that the height of each equilateral triangle is $\frac{1}{2}\sqrt{3}$.

Now we use *the area of a triangle is equal to* $\frac{1}{2} \times$ *base* $\times$ *height* to find that the area of one equilateral triangle is

$$\tfrac{1}{2} \times 1 \times \tfrac{1}{2}\sqrt{3} = \tfrac{1}{4}\sqrt{3}.$$

Hence the area of the whole star-shaped region is

$$12 \times \tfrac{1}{4}\sqrt{3} = 3\sqrt{3}.$$

Thus the area of the curvy unshaded region in figure 2 is equal to

$$3\sqrt{3} - \pi.$$

Appendix B

Sources of the problems

Every section B question from the JMO papers for the years 1999–2015 is used in part I of this book, either as an example or in an exercise (in a few cases the wording or layout of a question has been slightly altered).
The following tables give the sources of all the problems.

Examples		Exercise 4		Exercise 5		Exercise 6	
4	2005 B3	1.	2000 B1	1.	1999 B2	1.	2003 B1
5	2005 B4	2.	2006 B1	2.	2009 B2	2.	2005 B1
6	2001 B2	3.	2007 B1	3.	2015 B2	3.	2015 B1
7	2010 B2	4.	2009 B1	4.	2000 B3	4.	2000 B2
8	2012 B4	5.	2010 B1	5.	2001 B3	5.	2008 B2
9	2001 B5	6.	2012 B1	6.	2006 B3	6.	2004 B3
10	2012 B3	7.	2013 B1	7.	2008 B3	7.	2007 B3
12	2003 B3	8.	2005 B2	8.	2011 B4	8.	2009 B3
13	2009 B5	9.	2011 B2			9.	2000 B4
14	1999 B4	10.	2004 B2			10.	2010 B4

Exercise 7

1.	1999 B1
2.	2011 B1
3.	2012 B2
4.	2007 B4
5.	2000 B5
6.	2013 B5
7.	2014 B5

Exercise 8

1. 2001 B1
2. 2002 B1
3. 2014 B2
4. 2015 B3
5. 2003 B4

Exercise 9

1. 2001 B4
2. 1999 B5
3. 2005 B5
4. 2015 B5
5. 2003 B6
6. 2014 B6

Exercise 10

1. 2013 B2
2. 2010 B3
3. 2011 B3
4. 2011 B5
5. 2004 B6
6. 2006 B6
7. 2008 B6
8. 2010 B6
9. 2011 B6
10. 2015 B6

Exercise 11

1. 2008 B1
2. 2002 B2
3. 2003 B2
4. 2006 B2
5. 1999 B3
6. 2002 B4
7. 2008 B4
8. 2014 B4

Exercise 12

1. 2004 B1
2. 2014 B1
3. 2007 B2
4. 2013 B3
5. 2013 B4
6. 2015 B4
7. 2002 B5
8. 2010 B5
9. 2012 B5

Exercise 13

1. 2004 B5
2. 2006 B5
3. 1999 B6
4. 2000 B6
5. 2001 B6
6. 2002 B6
7. 2007 B6
8. 2009 B6
9. 2012 B6
10. 2013 B6

Exercise 14

1. 2002 B3
2. 2014 B3
3. 2004 B4
4. 2006 B4
5. 2009 B4
6. 2003 B5
7. 2007 B5
8. 2008 B5
9. 2005 B6

Glossary

The glossary collects together the explanations of some commonly used terms. If you are unable to find something here, then please try the index.

acute

> an acute angle measures less than 90°

allied angles

 angles like the two marked in the figure

alternate angles

 angles like the two marked in the figure

arc of a circle

 part of the circumference of a circle (such as shown in the figure)

bisect

> to bisect an object is to divide it into two equal parts

chord of a circle

a straight line segment (such as that shown in the figure) between two points on the circumference of a circle; the longest chord of a circle is a diameter

circumference of a circle

the perimeter of the circle

composite number

an integer greater than 1 which is not prime, that is, one which has divisors other than 1 and itself, such as $14 = 2 \times 7$, or $3551 = 53 \times 67$, or $75 = 3 \times 5 \times 5$

congruent

geometrical shapes are said to be congruent when they are identical

consecutive integers

two integers that differ by 1, such as 76, 77; a list of integers in which every pair is consecutive, for example, $-1, 0, 1, 2$

converse

the converse of the result 'if statement P is true then statement Q is true' is the result 'if statement Q is true then statement P is true'; note that the truth (or otherwise) of one result tells us nothing about the truth of the other—both might be true, just one might be true, or both might be false

corresponding angles

angles like the two marked in the figure

crossnumber

A crossnumber puzzle is like a crossword puzzle, except that the answers are numbers instead of words and each square contains one single digit. None of the answers starts with the digit 0.

diagonal of a polygon

a straight line segment (other than an edge) joining two vertices of the polygon

diameter of a circle

 a straight line segment (such as that shown in the figure) from one point on the circumference of a circle through the centre to another point on the circumference; also the length of this; the diameter is twice the radius

dissection

when a shape is divided into a number of smaller shapes; usually a polygon is divided by straight line segments into a number of smaller polygons

edge of a polygon

one of the straight line segments forming the boundary of the polygon

equation

a mathematical statement involving an equals sign

equilateral

in an equilateral shape all the edges have the same length; thus a rhombus is an equilateral quadrilateral

exterior angle of a polygon

 at each vertex of a polygon two sides meet; the exterior angle is the angle (such as that marked in the figure) between one side and the extension of the other side

hypotenuse

the side opposite the right angle in a right-angled triangle; the hypotenuse is the longest side of the triangle

interior angle of a polygon

at each vertex of a polygon two sides meet; the interior angle is the angle (such as that marked in the figure) inside the polygon between the sides

interior angles

another name for allied angles

isosceles triangle

a triangle with two sides of equal length

median of a triangle

the straight line joining a vertex of the triangle to the midpoint of the opposite side

mixed number

a number written in a form that is partly an integer and partly a fraction, such as $3\frac{4}{5}$

multiple

a multiple of a quantity is the number formed when you multiply that quantity by any integer

natural number

one of the counting numbers 1, 2, 3, ...

obtuse

an obtuse angle measures more than 90° and less than 180°

parallelogram

a quadrilateral in which each pair of opposite edges are parallel

perimeter

the boundary of a shape drawn in the plane; also the length of the boundary

perpendicular bisector

the perpendicular bisector of the straight line segment AB is the straight line at right angles to AB that passes through the midpoint of AB

perpendicular lines

two lines that cross at right angles

plane figure

a figure which lies in a plane, that is, a 'flat' figure

polygon

a closed shape that can be drawn in the plane and whose boundary consists of straight line segments

prime

an integer is prime when it is greater than 1 and it has no divisors other than 1 and itself; otherwise it is not prime

quadrilateral

a polygon with exactly four edges

radius of a circle

 a straight line segment (such as that shown in the figure) from the centre of a circle to a point on the circumference of the circle; also the length of this

ratio

a comparison of two quantities of the same kind (such as numbers, areas, speeds, ...) expressed in the form $a : b$

reflex

a reflex angle measures more than $180°$ and less than $360°$

regular polygon

a polygon in which all the edges have the same length and all the interior angles have the same size

rhombus

> a parallelogram with two adjacent sides equal in length

sector of a circle

> the region bounded by an arc of a circle and two radii, such as the shaded region shown

segment of a circle

> the region bounded by an arc of a circle and a chord, such as the shaded region shown

sequence

> a list of numbers in a particular order, such as the sequence of square integers 0, 1, 4, 9, 16, ...

theorem

> a statement that has been proved to be true through mathematical argument

trapezium

> a quadrilateral in which exactly one pair of opposite edges are parallel (so the other pair of edges are *not* parallel)

trisect

> to trisect an object is to divide it into three equal parts

unknown

> an unknown quantity in a problem, usually represented by a letter

variable

> another name for an unknown

vertex of a polygon

> the point at which two adjacent edges of the polygon meet

vertically opposite angles

angles that are 'opposite' each other across a 'vertex'—the point where a pair of straight lines cross—such as the two angles marked in the figure

vertices

> the plural of vertex

Index